Pray, Hope, & Don't Worry

Prayer Journal
For Catholic Women

A 52-week Guided Devotional
through Scripture & the Saints
to Overcome Anxiety

Sara A. Smith

HOLYWATERBOOKS

Pray, Hope, and Don't Worry Prayer Journal For Catholic Women
A 52-Week Guided Devotional through Scripture & the Saints to Overcome Anxiety
Copyright © 2020 Sara A. Smith; Scott L. Smith, editor

ISBN-13: 978-1-950782-16-1
All rights reserved.
Holy Water Books (Publisher)

HOLYWATERBOOKS

please check out our
other titles online at
www.holywaterbooks.com

Unless otherwise noted, all quotes from Scripture included in this book are from the Revised Standard Version – Catholic Edition (RSV-CE).

"Pray, hope, and don't worry.
Worry is useless.
God is merciful and will hear your prayer."

St. (Padre) Pio of Pietrelcina

Table of Contents

Foreward

Welcome to this prayer space!

We hope and pray you will find God here, and He will give you comfort.

The title comes from Padre Pio's famous quote, but it was another holy person that inspired this book. It was Chiara Corbello Petrillo, surely one of the Church's upcoming saints, who gave us the idea to create this prayer journal.

There are several **different ways to use this prayer journal**. Though the journal is designed for 52 *weeks* of guided prayer, it could also be used for 52 *days*. Just use each weekly section as a day section, instead. This could also be a resource for Lent if you just use it for 6 weeks or 40 days. We hope this journal will adapt itself to your needs.

Each of the 52 weeks (or days, if you prefer) includes a seven-step prayer sequence modeled after the *Examen* prayer of St. Ignatius. The seven steps are (1) Breathe, (2) Become aware of God's presence, (3) Thanksgiving, (4) Reflect, (5) Examination, (6) Contrition, and (7) Hope. Here is a more in-depth look at the purpose and significance of these steps:

1. The first step, **Breathe**, guides you through a breathing exercise that you can also use whenever you feel stressed, especially when you *first* begin to feel stressed. This breathing exercise can help you ward off a panic attack.

2. Take time to become aware of **God's presence**. Remember that He is closer to you than you are to yourself. He is with you right now, in the *now*. Let your soul come to rest, for as St. Augustine says, "Our hearts were made for You, O Lord, and they are restless until they rest in You."

3. **Thanksgiving:** A key to overcoming anxiety is re-orienting yourself to gratitude. That is, focusing less on your fears and more on God's gifts to you. *Lord, I realize that all, even myself, is a gift from you. Today, for what things am I most grateful?*

4. **Reflect** on the provided quote from the Saints or verse from Scripture. We chose these quotes and verses specifically to help you overcome anxiety. What words stand out to you? What comes into your mind as you reflect on the words? This is the meditative practice of *lectio divina*. Sit with these passages for five minutes or more each day through the week. Plant them in your mind, water them daily with reflection, and let them take root.

5. Ask the Lord to guide you through your day and week. Jesus will take you by the hand to **Examine** the moments and experiences of your life. Wait and see what bubbles up in your memories. What is Jesus trying to reveal to you? Jesus might be saying "I was there in that moment" but you did not see me, feel me, or hear me. Over time, this exercise will help you to know that Jesus never leaves your side and to *sense him* always there.

6. **Contrition**: Big or small, where, when, and how did sin creep into your day? Learning when you are tempted will help you remake your sin habits into virtues.

7. Learn to prayerfully anticipate the future in **Hope**. So much of our anxiety comes from unwarranted fear of the future. We dread events that may never come to pass. This exercise will help you shift your focus toward the good that is coming. The ultimate goal is to see God's presence in all things.

A Weekly Prayer is also included. We chose prayers that are focused on overcoming anxiety through gratitude, healing, empowering, and surrendering.

Lastly, each week (or day) also includes a page of Prayer Goals. The goals include a section to list your Prayer Intentions, a Goals Checklist, and a place to list your weekly Acts of Love and Sacrifice:

- **Prayer Intentions**: This is an opportunity to give your worries away to God. Imagine taking these intentions from your heart and placing them in Jesus' outstretched hands. Prayer especially for those people who stress you or have hurt you or a loved one. This is an amazing way to sever the chains that bind you to hurt.

- **Goals Checklist**: We provide some helpful prayer and sacramental practices to help you grow in the practice of the Catholic faith.

- **Small Things with Great Love**: Here is a place to list the times that you did a small act for another person with great love. When you do the dishes when it's not really your responsibility, when you apologize when it's not your fault, when you forgive the rude person at the grocery store - write it down here.

Lastly, be assured of our prayers for you, and maybe one day we will meet in Heaven ... where there's no such thing as fear and anxiety.

Totus tuus!

Sara & Scott Smith

first, Breathe

Breathe in ...
7 seconds.
Hold your breath ...
7 seconds.
Breathe out ...
7 seconds.

Repeat.

As many times
as you like.

second, Become aware of God's Presence

third, Thanksgiving

Lord, I realize that all, even myself, is a gift from you. Today, for what things am I most grateful?

"Pray, hope, and don't worry. Worry is useless.
God is merciful and will hear your prayer."
– St. (Padre) Pio

fifth,
Examination

Lord, open my eyes and ears to be more honest with myself. Show me what has been happening to me and in me this day. Today, how have I experienced your love?

sixth
Contrition

Today, what choices have been inadequate responses to your love?

seventh,
Hope

Lord, let me look with longing toward the future. How will I let you lead me to a brighter tomorrow?

Weekly
Prayer

"Take and Receive" Prayer

Take, Lord, and receive all my liberty,
My memory, my understanding,
And my entire will –
All that I have and call my own.
You have given it all to me.
To you, Lord, I return it.
Everything is yours;
Do with it what you will.
Give me only your love and your grace.
That is enough for me.
Amen.

Prayer Goals

Prayer Intentions

For whom or what do you want to pray this week? In particular, consider praying for those who frustrate or anger you, maybe even those who have harmed you or your loved ones.

_____
_____
_____
_____
_____
_____
_____

As St. (Mother) Teresa said, "Not all of us can do great things. But we can do ... *small things with great love*"

List your "small things" below:

_____
_____
_____
_____
_____
_____
_____
_____
_____
_____

Goals Checklist

Don't feel like you need to check all these boxes every week. Start with a goal of perhaps 2 or 3 and build from there.

- ☐ Daily Mass
- ☐ Confession
- ☐ Daily Rosary
- ☐ Daily Readings
- ☐ Divine Mercy Chaplet
- ☐ Novena
- ☐ Volunteer at Homeless Shelter or Food Bank *(or other Corporal Work of Mercy)*
- ☐ Morning Offering
- ☐ Evening Prayer or Liturgy of the Hours
- ☐ Fasting
- ☐ Read a Saint Biography
- ☐ Angelus
- ☐ Give alms or a donation

first, Breathe

Breathe in ...
7 seconds.
Hold your breath ...
7 seconds.
Breathe out ...
7 seconds.

Repeat.

As many times
as you like.

second, Become aware of God's Presence

third, Thanksgiving

Lord, I realize that all, even myself, is a gift from you. Today, for what things am I most grateful?

fourth, Reflect

"The past to mercy, the present to grace, the future to Providence ... Let us ask for grace ... each morning grace permits us ... to make it again to the evening.
– Chiara Corbella Petrillo, from *A Witness to Joy*

fifth, Examination

Lord, open my eyes and ears to be more honest with myself. Show me what has been happening to me and in me this day. Today, how have I experienced your love?

sixth, Contrition

Today, what choices have been inadequate responses to your love?

seventh, Hope

Lord, let me look with longing toward the future. How will I let you lead me to a brighter tomorrow?

Weekly
~ *Prayer* ~

Act of Hope

My God, relying on your
infinite goodness and promises,
I hope to obtain pardon of my sins,
Help of your grace,
And life everlasting
Through the merits of Jesus Christ,
My Lord and Redeemer
Amen.

Prayer Goals

Prayer Intentions

For whom or what do you want to pray this week? In particular, consider praying for those who frustrate or anger you, maybe even those who have harmed you or your loved ones.

_____
_____
_____
_____
_____
_____
_____

As St. (Mother) Teresa said, "Not all of us can do great things. But we can do ... *small things with great love*"

List your "small things" below:

_____
_____
_____
_____
_____
_____
_____
_____

Goals Checklist

Don't feel like you need to check all these boxes every week. Start with a goal of perhaps 2 or 3 and build from there.

- [ ] Daily Mass
- [ ] Confession
- [ ] Daily Rosary
- [ ] Daily Readings
- [ ] Divine Mercy Chaplet
- [ ] Novena
- [ ] Volunteer at Homeless Shelter or Food Bank
  (or other Corporal Work of Mercy)

- [ ] Morning Offering
- [ ] Evening Prayer or Liturgy of the Hours
- [ ] Fasting
- [ ] Read a Saint Biography
- [ ] Angelus
- [ ] Give alms or a donation

first, Breathe

Breathe in ...
7 seconds.
Hold your breath ...
7 seconds.
Breathe out ...
7 seconds.

Repeat.

As many times
as you like.

second, Become aware of God's Presence

third, Thanksgiving

Lord, I realize that all, even myself, is a gift from you. Today, for what things am I most grateful?

"Who except God can give you peace?
Has the world ever been able to satisfy the heart?"
- St. Gerard Majella

fifth,
Examination

Lord, open my eyes and ears to be more honest with myself. Show me what has been happening to me and in me this day. Today, how have I experienced your love?

_____
_____
_____
_____
_____
_____
_____
_____
_____
_____

sixth
Contrition

Today, what choices have been inadequate responses to your love?

_____
_____
_____
_____
_____
_____

seventh,
Hope

Lord, let me look with longing toward the future. How will I let you lead me to a brighter tomorrow?

_____
_____
_____
_____
_____
_____

Weekly
Prayer

Serenity Prayer

God, grant me the serenity
to accept the things I cannot change,
the courage to change the things I can,
and the wisdom to know the difference.
Living one day at a time,
enjoying one moment at a time;
accepting hardship as a pathway to peace;
taking, as Jesus did,
this sinful world as it is,
not as I would have it;
trusting that You will make all things right
if I surrender to Your will;
so that I may be reasonably happy in this life
and supremely happy with You
forever in the next.
Amen.

Prayer Goals

Prayer Intentions

For whom or what do you want to pray this week? In particular, consider praying for those who frustrate or anger you, maybe even those who have harmed you or your loved ones.

_____
_____
_____
_____
_____
_____
_____

As St. (Mother) Teresa said, "Not all of us can do great things. But we can do ... *small things with great love*"

List your "small things" below:

_____
_____
_____
_____
_____
_____
_____
_____
_____
_____
_____
_____

Goals Checklist

Don't feel like you need to check all these boxes every week. Start with a goal of perhaps 2 or 3 and build from there.

☐ Daily Mass

☐ Confession

☐ Daily Rosary

☐ Daily Readings

☐ Divine Mercy Chaplet

☐ Novena

☐ Volunteer at Homeless Shelter or Food Bank
(or other Corporal Work of Mercy)

☐ Morning Offering

☐ Evening Prayer or Liturgy of the Hours

☐ Fasting

☐ Read a Saint Biography

☐ Angelus

☐ Give alms or a donation

first, Breathe

Breathe in ...
7 seconds.
Hold your breath ...
7 seconds.
Breathe out ...
7 seconds.

Repeat.

As many times
as you like.

third, Thanksgiving

Lord, I realize that all, even myself, is a gift from you. Today, for what things am I most grateful?

second, Become aware of God's Presence

"Let go of your plans. The first hour of your morning belongs to God. Tackle the day's work that he charges you with, and he will give you the power to accomplish it."
– St. Edith Stein

fifth,
Examination

Lord, open my eyes and ears to be more honest with myself. Show me what has been happening to me and in me this day. Today, how have I experienced your love?

_____
_____
_____
_____
_____
_____
_____
_____
_____
_____

sixth,
Contrition

Today, what choices have been inadequate responses to your love?

_____
_____
_____
_____
_____
_____
_____

seventh,
Hope

Lord, let me look with longing toward the future. How will I let you lead me to a brighter tomorrow?

_____
_____
_____
_____
_____
_____
_____

Weekly
Prayer

Litany of Humility

O Jesus, meek and humble of heart, *Hear me.*
From the desire of being esteemed, *Deliver me, O Jesus.*
From the desire of being loved, *Deliver me, O Jesus.*
From the desire of being extolled, *Deliver me, O Jesus.*
From the desire of being honored, *Deliver me, O Jesus.*
From the desire of being praised, *Deliver me, O Jesus.*
From the desire of being preferred to others, *Deliver me, O Jesus.*
From the desire of being consulted, *Deliver me, O Jesus.*
From the desire of being approved, *Deliver me, O Jesus.*
From the fear of being humiliated, *Deliver me, O Jesus.*
From the fear of being despised, *Deliver me, O Jesus.*
From the fear of suffering rebukes, *Deliver me, O Jesus.*
From the fear of being calumniated, *Deliver me, O Jesus.*
From the fear of being forgotten, *Deliver me, O Jesus.*
From the fear of being ridiculed, *Deliver me, O Jesus.*
From the fear of being wronged, *Deliver me, O Jesus.*
From the fear of being suspected, *Deliver me, O Jesus.*
That others may be loved more than I,
Jesus, grant me the grace to desire it.
That others may be esteemed more than I,
Jesus, grant me the grace to desire it.
That, in the opinion of the world, others may increase and I may decrease,
Jesus, grant me the grace to desire it.
That others may be chosen and I set aside,
Jesus, grant me the grace to desire it.
That others may be praised and I go unnoticed,
Jesus, grant me the grace to desire it.
That others may be preferred to me in everything,
Jesus, grant me the grace to desire it.
That others may become holier than I, provided that I may become as holy as I
should, *Jesus, grant me the grace to desire it.*
Amen.

Prayer Goals

Prayer Intentions

For whom or what do you want to pray this week? In particular, consider praying for those who frustrate or anger you, maybe even those who have harmed you or your loved ones.

_____
_____
_____
_____
_____
_____
_____
_____
_____

As St. (Mother) Teresa said, "Not all of us can do great things. But we can do ... *small things with great love*"

List your "small things" below:

_____
_____
_____
_____
_____
_____
_____
_____
_____
_____

Goals Checklist

Don't feel like you need to check all these boxes every week. Start with a goal of perhaps 2 or 3 and build from there.

- ☐ Daily Mass
- ☐ Confession
- ☐ Daily Rosary
- ☐ Daily Readings
- ☐ Divine Mercy Chaplet
- ☐ Novena
- ☐ Volunteer at Homeless Shelter or Food Bank (or other Corporal Work of Mercy)

- ☐ Morning Offering
- ☐ Evening Prayer or Liturgy of the Hours
- ☐ Fasting
- ☐ Read a Saint Biography
- ☐ Angelus
- ☐ Give alms or a donation

first, Breathe

Breathe in ...
7 seconds.
Hold your breath ...
7 seconds.
Breathe out ...
7 seconds.

Repeat.

As many times
as you like.

second, Become aware of God's Presence

third, Thanksgiving

Lord, I realize that all, even myself, is a gift from you. Today, for what things am I most grateful?

But the Lord answered her, "Martha, Martha, you are anxious and troubled about many things; one thing is needful. Mary has chosen the good portion, which shall not be taken away from her."
– Luke 10:41–42

fifth,
Examination

Lord, open my eyes and ears to be more honest with myself. Show me what has been happening to me and in me this day. Today, how have I experienced your love?

sixth
Contrition

Today, what choices have been inadequate responses to your love?

seventh,
Hope

Lord, let me look with longing toward the future. How will I let you lead me to a brighter tomorrow?

Weekly
Prayer

Prayer for Calm

My Lord and my God,
I do not know what will happen to me today,
But what I do know is that
Nothing will happen to me today
That You and I together cannot handle.
This thought is enough
To bring me to face the day in peace.
I adore you in your wisdom and love.
I commend myself into your hands with the
complete trust.
Amen.

Prayer Goals

Prayer Intentions

For whom or what do you want to pray this week? In particular, consider praying for those who frustrate or anger you, maybe even those who have harmed you or your loved ones.

_____
_____
_____
_____
_____
_____
_____
_____
_____

As St. (Mother) Teresa said, "Not all of us can do great things. But we can do ... *small things with great love*"

List your "small things" below:

_____
_____
_____
_____
_____
_____
_____
_____
_____

Goals Checklist

Don't feel like you need to check all these boxes every week. Start with a goal of perhaps 2 or 3 and build from there.

- ☐ Daily Mass
- ☐ Confession
- ☐ Daily Rosary
- ☐ Daily Readings
- ☐ Divine Mercy Chaplet
- ☐ Novena
- ☐ Volunteer at Homeless Shelter or Food Bank
  (or other Corporal Work of Mercy)

- ☐ Morning Offering
- ☐ Evening Prayer or Liturgy of the Hours
- ☐ Fasting
- ☐ Read a Saint Biography
- ☐ Angelus
- ☐ Give alms or a donation

first, Breathe

Breathe in ...
7 seconds.
Hold your breath ...
7 seconds.
Breathe out ...
7 seconds.

Repeat.

As many times
as you like.

second, Become aware of God's Presence

third, Thanksgiving

Lord, I realize that all, even myself, is a gift from you. Today, for what things am I most grateful?

fourth,
Reflect

Anxiety in a man's heart weighs him down,
but a good word makes him glad.
Proverbs 12:25

fifth,
Examination

Lord, open my eyes and ears to be more honest with myself. Show me what has been happening to me and in me this day. Today, how have I experienced your love?

_____
_____
_____
_____
_____
_____
_____
_____
_____
_____
_____

sixth
Contrition

Today, what choices have been inadequate responses to your love?

_____
_____
_____
_____
_____
_____

seventh,
Hope

Lord, let me look with longing toward the future. How will I let you lead me to a brighter tomorrow?

_____
_____
_____
_____
_____
_____

Weekly
Prayer

Litany of Trust, Part One
From the Sisters of Life

From the belief that I have to earn Your love,
Deliver me, Jesus.
From the fear that I am unlovable,
Deliver me, Jesus.
From the false security that I have what it takes,
Deliver me, Jesus.
From the fear that trusting You will leave me more destitute,
Deliver me, Jesus.
From all suspicion of Your words and promises,
Deliver me, Jesus.
From the rebellion against childlike dependency on You,
Deliver me, Jesus.
From refusals and reluctances in accepting Your will,
Deliver me, Jesus.
From anxiety about the future,
Deliver me, Jesus.
From resentment or excessive preoccupation with the past,
Deliver me, Jesus.
From restless self-seeking in the present moment,
Deliver me, Jesus.
From disbelief in Your love and presence,
Deliver me, Jesus.
From the fear of being asked to give more than I have,
Deliver me, Jesus.
From the belief that my life has no meaning or worth,
Deliver me, Jesus.
From the fear of what love demands,
Deliver me, Jesus.
From discouragement,
Deliver me, Jesus.

Prayer Goals

Prayer Intentions

For whom or what do you want to pray this week? In particular, consider praying for those who frustrate or anger you, maybe even those who have harmed you or your loved ones.

_____
_____
_____
_____
_____
_____
_____
_____
_____
_____

As St. (Mother) Teresa said, "Not all of us can do great things. But we can do ... *small things with great love*"

List your "small things" below:

_____
_____
_____
_____
_____
_____
_____
_____
_____
_____
_____

Goals Checklist

Don't feel like you need to check all these boxes every week. Start with a goal of perhaps 2 or 3 and build from there.

- ☐ Daily Mass
- ☐ Confession
- ☐ Daily Rosary
- ☐ Daily Readings
- ☐ Divine Mercy Chaplet
- ☐ Novena
- ☐ Volunteer at Homeless Shelter or Food Bank (or other Corporal Work of Mercy)
- ☐ Morning Offering
- ☐ Evening Prayer or Liturgy of the Hours
- ☐ Fasting
- ☐ Read a Saint Biography
- ☐ Angelus
- ☐ Give alms or a donation

first,
Breathe

Breathe in ...
7 seconds.
Hold your breath ...
7 seconds.
Breathe out ...
7 seconds.

Repeat.

As many times
as you like.

second,
Become aware of
God's Presence

third,
Thanksgiving

Lord, I realize that all, even myself, is a gift from you. Today, for what things am I most grateful?

fourth, Reflect

"Do not have any anxiety about the future.
Leave everything in God's hands for he will take care of you."
– St. John Baptiste de la Salle

fifth, Examination

Lord, open my eyes and ears to be more honest with myself. Show me what has been happening to me and in me this day. Today, how have I experienced your love?

_____
_____
_____
_____
_____
_____
_____
_____
_____
_____
_____
_____

sixth Contrition

Today, what choices have been inadequate responses to your love?

_____
_____
_____
_____
_____
_____
_____

seventh, Hope

Lord, let me look with longing toward the future. How will I let you lead me to a brighter tomorrow?

_____
_____
_____
_____
_____
_____
_____

Weekly *Prayer*

Litany of Trust, Part Two
From the Sisters of Life

That You are continually holding me, sustaining me, loving me,
Jesus, I trust in You.
That Your love goes deeper than my sins and failings and transforms me,
Jesus, I trust in You.
That not knowing what tomorrow brings is an invitation to lean on You,
Jesus, I trust in You.
That You are with me in my suffering, *Jesus, I trust in You.*
That my suffering, united to Your own, will bear fruit in this life and the
next, *Jesus, I trust in You.*
That You will not leave me orphan, that You are present in Your Church,
Jesus, I trust in You.
That Your plan is better than anything else, *Jesus, I trust in You.*
That You always hear me and in Your goodness always respond to me
Jesus, I trust in You.
That You give me the grace to accept forgiveness and to forgive others
Jesus, I trust in You.
That You give me all the strength I need for what is asked
Jesus, I trust in You.
That my life is a gift, *Jesus, I trust in You.*
That You will teach me to trust You, *Jesus, I trust in You.*
That You are my Lord and my God, *Jesus, I trust in You.*
That I am Your beloved one, *Jesus, I trust in You.*

Prayer Goals

Prayer Intentions

For whom or what do you want to pray this week? In particular, consider praying for those who frustrate or anger you, maybe even those who have harmed you or your loved ones.

_____
_____
_____
_____
_____
_____
_____
_____
_____
_____
_____
_____

> As St. (Mother) Teresa said, "Not all of us can do great things. But we can do ... *small things with great love*"

List your "small things" below:

_____
_____
_____
_____
_____
_____
_____

Goals Checklist

Don't feel like you need to check all these boxes every week. Start with a goal of perhaps 2 or 3 and build from there.

- ☐ Daily Mass
- ☐ Confession
- ☐ Daily Rosary
- ☐ Daily Readings
- ☐ Divine Mercy Chaplet
- ☐ Novena
- ☐ Volunteer at Homeless Shelter or Food Bank (or other Corporal Work of Mercy)
- ☐ Morning Offering
- ☐ Evening Prayer or Liturgy of the Hours
- ☐ Fasting
- ☐ Read a Saint Biography
- ☐ Angelus
- ☐ Give alms or a donation

_____
_____
_____
_____
_____

first, Breathe

Breathe in ...
7 seconds.
Hold your breath ...
7 seconds.
Breathe out ...
7 seconds.

Repeat.

As many times
as you like.

second, Become aware of God's Presence

third, Thanksgiving

Lord, I realize that all, even myself, is a gift from you. Today, for what things am I most grateful?

"The stillness of prayer is the most essential condition for fruitful action.
Before all else, the disciple kneels down."
- St. Gianna Beretta Molla

fifth,
Examination

Lord, open my eyes and ears to be more honest with myself. Show me what has been happening to me and in me this day. Today, how have I experienced your love?

_____
_____
_____
_____
_____
_____
_____
_____
_____
_____
_____

sixth,
Contrition

Today, what choices have been inadequate responses to your love?

_____
_____
_____
_____
_____
_____

seventh,
Hope

Lord, let me look with longing toward the future. How will I let you lead me to a brighter tomorrow?

_____
_____
_____
_____
_____
_____

Weekly
Prayer

Prayer for Peace and Calm
From John Greenleaf Whittier

Dear Lord and Father of humankind,
Forgive our foolish ways;
Reclothe us in our rightful mind,
In purer lives Thy service find,
In deeper reverence, praise.

Drop Thy still dews of quietness,
Till all our strivings cease;
Take from our souls the strain and stress,
And let our ordered lives confess
The beauty of Thy peace.

Breathe through the heats of our desire
Thy coolness and Thy balm;
Let sense be dumb, let flesh retire;
Speak through the earthquake, wind, and fire,
O still, small voice of calm.

Prayer Goals

Prayer Intentions

For whom or what do you want to pray this week? In particular, consider praying for those who frustrate or anger you, maybe even those who have harmed you or your loved ones.

_____
_____
_____
_____
_____
_____
_____
_____
_____
_____

As St. (Mother) Teresa said, "Not all of us can do great things. But we can do ... *small things with great love*"

List your "small things" below:

_____
_____
_____
_____
_____
_____
_____
_____
_____
_____
_____
_____
_____

Goals Checklist

Don't feel like you need to check all these boxes every week. Start with a goal of perhaps 2 or 3 and build from there.

- [ ] Daily Mass
- [ ] Confession
- [ ] Daily Rosary
- [ ] Daily Readings
- [ ] Divine Mercy Chaplet
- [ ] Novena
- [ ] Volunteer at Homeless Shelter or Food Bank (or other Corporal Work of Mercy)
- [ ] Morning Offering
- [ ] Evening Prayer or Liturgy of the Hours
- [ ] Fasting
- [ ] Read a Saint Biography
- [ ] Angelus
- [ ] Give alms or a donation

first, *Breathe*

Breathe in ...
7 seconds.
Hold your breath ...
7 seconds.
Breathe out ...
7 seconds.

Repeat.

As many times
as you like.

second, Become aware of *God's Presence*

third, *Thanksgiving*

Lord, I realize that all, even myself, is a gift from you. Today, for what things am I most grateful?

fourth,
Reflect

In peace I will lie down and sleep;
for Thou alone, O Lord, makest me dwell in safety.
– Psalm 4:8

fifth,
Examination

Lord, open my eyes and ears to be more honest with myself. Show me what has been happening to me and in me this day. Today, how have I experienced your love?

_____
_____
_____
_____
_____
_____
_____
_____
_____
_____
_____

sixth,
Contrition

Today, what choices have been inadequate responses to your love?

_____
_____
_____
_____
_____
_____
_____
_____

seventh,
Hope

Lord, let me look with longing toward the future. How will I let you lead me to a brighter tomorrow?

_____
_____
_____
_____
_____
_____
_____
_____

Weekly
Prayer

A Prayer for Soothing Panic Attacks

Dear God,
I come before You to
Lay my panic and anxiety at Your feet.
When I'm crushed by my fears and worries,
remind me of Your power and Your grace.
Fill me with Your peace
As I trust in You and You alone.
I know I can't beat this on my own,
but I also know that I have You, Lord,
And You have already paid the ultimate price
To carry my burdens.
For this I thank you.
Amen.

Prayer Goals

Prayer Intentions

For whom or what do you want to pray this week? In particular, consider praying for those who frustrate or anger you, maybe even those who have harmed you or your loved ones.

_____
_____
_____
_____
_____
_____
_____
_____

As St. (Mother) Teresa said, "Not all of us can do great things. But we can do ... *small things with great love*"

List your "small things" below:

_____
_____
_____
_____
_____
_____
_____
_____
_____

Goals Checklist

Don't feel like you need to check all these boxes every week. Start with a goal of perhaps 2 or 3 and build from there.

- [ ] Daily Mass
- [ ] Confession
- [ ] Daily Rosary
- [ ] Daily Readings
- [ ] Divine Mercy Chaplet
- [ ] Novena
- [ ] Volunteer at Homeless Shelter or Food Bank (or other Corporal Work of Mercy)

- [ ] Morning Offering
- [ ] Evening Prayer or Liturgy of the Hours
- [ ] Fasting
- [ ] Read a Saint Biography
- [ ] Angelus
- [ ] Give alms or a donation

first,
Breathe

Breathe in ...
7 seconds.
Hold your breath ...
7 seconds.
Breathe out ...
7 seconds.

Repeat.

As many times
as you like.

second,
Become aware of
God's Presence

third,
Thanksgiving

Lord, I realize that all, even myself, is a gift from you. Today, for what things am I most grateful?

fourth,
Reflect

"If we have any natural defect, either in mind or body, let us not grieve and feel sorry for ourselves. Who can tell whether, if we had been given a larger share of ability or stronger health, or greater wealth, we would have possessed them to the destruction of our soul!"
– St. Alphonsus Liquori

fifth, Examination

Lord, open my eyes and ears to be more honest with myself. Show me what has been happening to me and in me this day. Today, how have I experienced your love?

_____
_____
_____
_____
_____
_____
_____
_____
_____
_____
_____
_____

sixth, Contrition

Today, what choices have been inadequate responses to your love?

_____
_____
_____
_____
_____
_____

seventh, Hope

Lord, let me look with longing toward the future. How will I let you lead me to a brighter tomorrow?

_____
_____
_____
_____
_____
_____

Weekly
Prayer

Your Peace

God,
Who is more than we can ever comprehend,
Help us to seek You,
And You alone.
Help us to stand before all that we could do
And seek what You would do,
And do that.
Lift from us our need
To achieve all that we can be
And instead,
Surrender to what You can be in us.
Give us ways to refrain from the busyness
That will put us on edge and off center,
Give us today Your peace.
Amen.

Prayer Goals

Prayer Intentions

For whom or what do you want to pray this week? In particular, consider praying for those who frustrate or anger you, maybe even those who have harmed you or your loved ones.

_____
_____
_____
_____
_____
_____
_____
_____

As St. (Mother) Teresa said, "Not all of us can do great things. But we can do ... *small things with great love*"

List your "small things" below:

_____
_____
_____
_____
_____
_____
_____
_____
_____
_____
_____

Goals Checklist

Don't feel like you need to check all these boxes every week. Start with a goal of perhaps 2 or 3 and build from there.

- ☐ Daily Mass
- ☐ Confession
- ☐ Daily Rosary
- ☐ Daily Readings
- ☐ Divine Mercy Chaplet
- ☐ Novena
- ☐ Volunteer at Homeless Shelter or Food Bank (or other Corporal Work of Mercy)
- ☐ Morning Offering
- ☐ Evening Prayer or Liturgy of the Hours
- ☐ Fasting
- ☐ Read a Saint Biography
- ☐ Angelus
- ☐ Give alms or a donation

first, Breathe

Breathe in ...
7 seconds.
Hold your breath ...
7 seconds.
Breathe out ...
7 seconds.

Repeat.

As many times
as you like.

second, Become aware of God's Presence

third, Thanksgiving

Lord, I realize that all, even myself, is a gift from you. Today, for what things am I most grateful?

fourth,
Reflect

"Go forth in peace, for you have followed the good road. Go forth without fear, for he who created you has made you holy, has always protected you, and loves you as a mother. Blessed be you, my God, for having created me."
– St. Clare of Assisi

fifth,
Examination

Lord, open my eyes and ears to be more honest with myself. Show me what has been happening to me and in me this day. Today, how have I experienced your love?

_____
_____
_____
_____
_____
_____
_____
_____
_____
_____
_____

sixth,
Contrition

Today, what choices have been inadequate responses to your love?

_____
_____
_____
_____
_____
_____

seventh,
Hope

Lord, let me look with longing toward the future. How will I let you lead me to a brighter tomorrow?

_____
_____
_____
_____
_____
_____

Weekly
Prayer

Prayer for Strength
From Psalm 27:1b

Dear Jesus,
You are the strength of my life;
You are my rock, my fortress and my protector;
Therefore, whom shall I be afraid?
You are my shield,
My strong-tower and my stronghold.
I will call to You because
You are worthy to be praised.
So, Father,
I thank you for being my strength
And My God in whom I trust.
Amen.

Prayer Goals

Prayer Intentions

For whom or what do you want to pray this week? In particular, consider praying for those who frustrate or anger you, maybe even those who have harmed you or your loved ones.

_____
_____
_____
_____
_____
_____
_____
_____
_____

As St. (Mother) Teresa said, "Not all of us can do great things. But we can do ...
small things with great love"

List your "small things" below:

_____
_____
_____
_____
_____
_____
_____
_____
_____
_____
_____

Goals Checklist

Don't feel like you need to check all these boxes every week. Start with a goal of perhaps 2 or 3 and build from there.

- ☐ Daily Mass
- ☐ Confession
- ☐ Daily Rosary
- ☐ Daily Readings
- ☐ Divine Mercy Chaplet
- ☐ Novena
- ☐ Volunteer at Homeless Shelter or Food Bank (or other Corporal Work of Mercy)
- ☐ Morning Offering
- ☐ Evening Prayer or Liturgy of the Hours
- ☐ Fasting
- ☐ Read a Saint Biography
- ☐ Angelus
- ☐ Give alms or a donation

first, Breathe

Breathe in ...
7 seconds.
Hold your breath ...
7 seconds.
Breathe out ...
7 seconds.

Repeat.

As many times
as you like.

second, Become aware of God's Presence

third, Thanksgiving

Lord, I realize that all, even myself, is a gift from you. Today, for what things am I most grateful?

fourth,
Reflect

"Therefore do not be anxious about tomorrow,
For tomorrow will be anxious for itself.
Let the day's own trouble be sufficient for the day."
– Matthew 6:34

fifth,
Examination

Lord, open my eyes and ears to be more honest with myself. Show me what has been happening to me and in me this day. Today, how have I experienced your love?

_____
_____
_____
_____
_____
_____
_____
_____
_____
_____

sixth
Contrition

Today, what choices have been inadequate responses to your love?

seventh,
Hope

Lord, let me look with longing toward the future. How will I let you lead me to a brighter tomorrow?

_____
_____
_____
_____
_____
_____

Weekly *Prayer*

Prayer of St. Francis

Lord, make me an instrument of your peace:
where there is hatred, let me sow love;
where there is injury, pardon;
where there is doubt, faith;
where there is despair, hope;
where there is darkness, light;
where there is sadness, joy.

O divine Master, grant that I may not so much seek
to be consoled as to console,
to be understood as to understand,
to be loved as to love.
For it is in giving that we receive,
it is in pardoning that we are pardoned,
and it is in dying that we are born to eternal life.
Amen.

Prayer Goals

Prayer Intentions

For whom or what do you want to pray this week? In particular, consider praying for those who frustrate or anger you, maybe even those who have harmed you or your loved ones.

As St. (Mother) Teresa said, "Not all of us can do great things. But we can do ...
small things with great love"

List your "small things" below:

Goals Checklist

Don't feel like you need to check all these boxes every week. Start with a goal of perhaps 2 or 3 and build from there.

- [ ] Daily Mass
- [ ] Confession
- [ ] Daily Rosary
- [ ] Daily Readings
- [ ] Divine Mercy Chaplet
- [ ] Novena
- [ ] Volunteer at Homeless Shelter or Food Bank
  (or other Corporal Work of Mercy)
- [ ] Morning Offering
- [ ] Evening Prayer or Liturgy of the Hours
- [ ] Fasting
- [ ] Read a Saint Biography
- [ ] Angelus
- [ ] Give alms or a donation

Week Thirteen

first, Breathe

Breathe in ...
7 seconds.
Hold your breath ...
7 seconds.
Breathe out ...
7 seconds.

Repeat.

As many times
as you like.

second, Become aware of God's Presence

third, Thanksgiving

Lord, I realize that all, even myself, is a gift from you. Today, for what things am I most grateful?

fourth,
Reflect

Cast all your anxieties on Him, for He cares about you.
1 Peter 5:7

fifth,
Examination

Lord, open my eyes and ears to be more honest with myself. Show me what has been happening to me and in me this day. Today, how have I experienced your love?

_____
_____
_____
_____
_____
_____
_____
_____
_____
_____
_____
_____
_____

sixth,
Contrition

Today, what choices have been inadequate responses to your love?

_____
_____
_____
_____
_____
_____
_____

seventh,
Hope

Lord, let me look with longing toward the future. How will I let you lead me to a brighter tomorrow?

_____
_____
_____
_____
_____
_____
_____

Weekly
Prayer

I Want To Be Available

Holy and perfect God,
You know I want to be available.
Help that desire sink deeply enough
Into my being
For me to actually change
And to say "no" to a least one worthy,
But not urgent, task today.
Give me the ability to be open
To the life I am leading;
Not the one I am planning to lead.

Prayer Goals

Prayer Intentions

For whom or what do you want to pray this week? In particular, consider praying for those who frustrate or anger you, maybe even those who have harmed you or your loved ones.

As St. (Mother) Teresa said, "Not all of us can do great things. But we can do ...
small things with great love"

List your "small things" below:

Goals Checklist

Don't feel like you need to check all these boxes every week. Start with a goal of perhaps 2 or 3 and build from there.

- ☐ Daily Mass
- ☐ Confession
- ☐ Daily Rosary
- ☐ Daily Readings
- ☐ Divine Mercy Chaplet
- ☐ Novena
- ☐ Volunteer at Homeless Shelter or Food Bank
  (or other Corporal Work of Mercy)

- ☐ Morning Offering
- ☐ Evening Prayer or Liturgy of the Hours
- ☐ Fasting
- ☐ Read a Saint Biography
- ☐ Angelus
- ☐ Give alms or a donation

Week Fourteen

first, Breathe

Breathe in ...
7 seconds.
Hold your breath ...
7 seconds.
Breathe out ...
7 seconds.

Repeat.

As many times
as you like.

second, Become aware of God's Presence

third, Thanksgiving

Lord, I realize that all, even myself, is a gift from you. Today, for what things am I most grateful?

fourth,
Reflect

"What really matters in life is that we are loved by Christ and that we love Him in return. In comparison to the love of Jesus, everything else is secondary. And, without the love of Jesus, everything is useless."
– St. Pope John Paul II

fifth,
Examination

Lord, open my eyes and ears to be more honest with myself. Show me what has been happening to me and in me this day. Today, how have I experienced your love?

_____
_____
_____
_____
_____
_____
_____

sixth
Contrition

Today, what choices have been inadequate responses to your love?

_____
_____
_____
_____
_____

seventh,
Hope

Lord, let me look with longing toward the future. How will I let you lead me to a brighter tomorrow?

_____
_____
_____
_____
_____

Weekly *Prayer*

A Prayer for Calming a Troubled Heart

Loving God,
Please grant me peace of mind
And calm my troubled heart.
My soul is like a turbulent sea.
I can't seem to find my balance,
So I stumble and worry constantly.

Give me the strength and clarity of mind
To find my purpose and walk the path
You've laid out for me.
I trust Your Love, God,
And know that You will heal this stress.
Just as the sun rises each day
Against the dark of night.
Please bring me clarity with the light of God.
In Your Name I pray.
Amen.

Prayer Goals

Prayer Intentions

For whom or what do you want to pray this week? In particular, consider praying for those who frustrate or anger you, maybe even those who have harmed you or your loved ones.

_____
_____
_____
_____
_____
_____
_____
_____
_____

As St. (Mother) Teresa said, "Not all of us can do great things. But we can do ... *small things with great love*"

List your "small things" below:

_____
_____
_____
_____
_____
_____
_____
_____
_____
_____

Goals Checklist

Don't feel like you need to check all these boxes every week. Start with a goal of perhaps 2 or 3 and build from there.

- ☐ Daily Mass
- ☐ Confession
- ☐ Daily Rosary
- ☐ Daily Readings
- ☐ Divine Mercy Chaplet
- ☐ Novena
- ☐ Volunteer at Homeless Shelter or Food Bank (or other Corporal Work of Mercy)
- ☐ Morning Offering
- ☐ Evening Prayer or Liturgy of the Hours
- ☐ Fasting
- ☐ Read a Saint Biography
- ☐ Angelus
- ☐ Give alms or a donation

first, Breathe

Breathe in ...
7 seconds.
Hold your breath ...
7 seconds.
Breathe out ...
7 seconds.

Repeat.

As many times
as you like.

second, Become aware of God's Presence

third, Thanksgiving

Lord, I realize that all, even myself, is a gift from you. Today, for what things am I most grateful?

"I will not mistrust Him, Meg, though I shall feel myself weakening and on the verge of being overcome with fear. I shall remember, how Saint Peter at a blast of wind, began to sink because of his lack of faith and I shall do as he did, call upon Christ and pray to Him for help. And then I trust He shall place His holy hand on me and in the stormy seas, hold me up from drowning."
– St. Thomas More (writing to his wife)

fifth,
Examination

Lord, open my eyes and ears to be more honest with myself. Show me what has been happening to me and in me this day. Today, how have I experienced your love?

_____
_____
_____
_____
_____
_____
_____
_____
_____
_____
_____

sixth,
Contrition

Today, what choices have been inadequate responses to your love?

seventh,
Hope

Lord, let me look with longing toward the future. How will I let you lead me to a brighter tomorrow?

_____
_____
_____
_____
_____
_____

Weekly
Prayer

A Prayer for Christ's Peace

Lord, please put Your peace in my heart.
I'm worried and anxious.
My mind races and obsesses.
I can't help thinking about my problems.
And the more I think about them,
The more depressed I become.
I feel like I'm sinking down in quicksand
And can't get out.
Calm me, Lord.
Slow me down,
Put Your peace in my heart.

No matter what problem I have, Lord,
You are bigger,
You are more powerful than it is.
So I bring my problem to You.
I know what I want.
I know my will, but I do not know Yours.
I do not know how You will use this problem for my salvation.
I do not know what good You will work from this evil.
But I trust You.
I trust Your goodness and Your wisdom.
So I place myself in Your hands.
Please fill my heart with peace.
Amen.

Prayer Goals

Prayer Intentions

For whom or what do you want to pray this week? In particular, consider praying for those who frustrate or anger you, maybe even those who have harmed you or your loved ones.

_____
_____
_____
_____
_____
_____
_____
_____

As St. (Mother) Teresa said, "Not all of us can do great things. But we can do ... *small things with great love*"

List your "small things" below:

_____
_____
_____
_____
_____
_____
_____
_____
_____
_____

Goals Checklist

Don't feel like you need to check all these boxes every week. Start with a goal of perhaps 2 or 3 and build from there.

- ☐ Daily Mass
- ☐ Confession
- ☐ Daily Rosary
- ☐ Daily Readings
- ☐ Divine Mercy Chaplet
- ☐ Novena
- ☐ Volunteer at Homeless Shelter or Food Bank (or other Corporal Work of Mercy)

- ☐ Morning Offering
- ☐ Evening Prayer or Liturgy of the Hours
- ☐ Fasting
- ☐ Read a Saint Biography
- ☐ Angelus
- ☐ Give alms or a donation

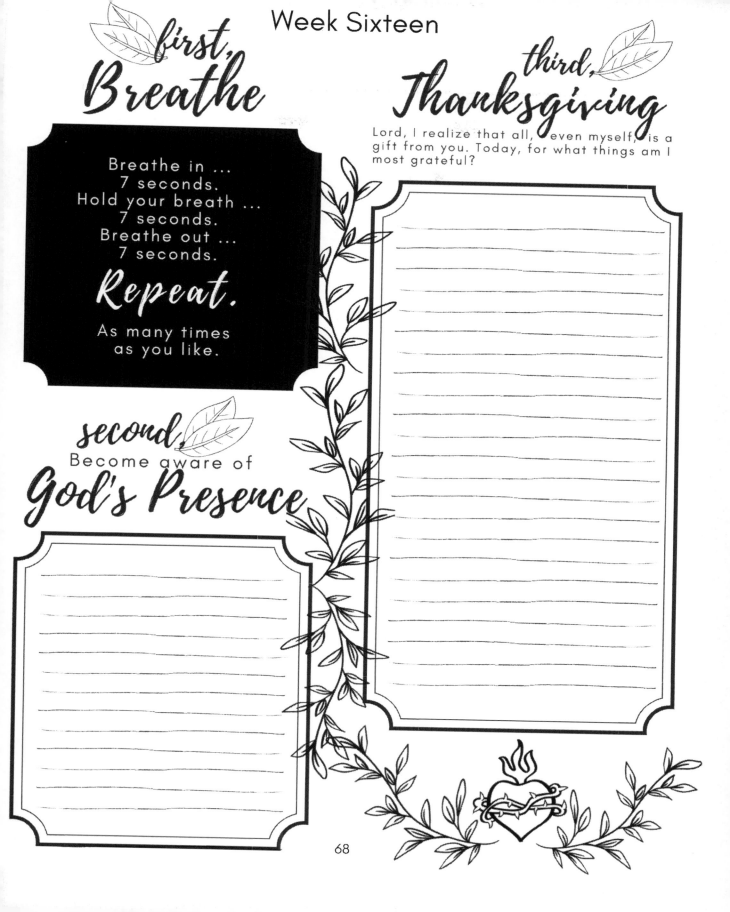

first, Breathe

Breathe in ...
7 seconds.
Hold your breath ...
7 seconds.
Breathe out ...
7 seconds.

Repeat.

As many times
as you like.

second, Become aware of God's Presence

third, Thanksgiving

Lord, I realize that all, even myself, is a gift from you. Today, for what things am I most grateful?

fourth, Reflect

But they who wait for the Lord shall renew their strength,
they shall mount up with wings like eagles,
they shall run and not be weary,
they shall walk and not faint.
Isaiah 40:31

fifth, Examination

Lord, open my eyes and ears to be more honest with myself. Show me what has been happening to me and in me this day. Today, how have I experienced your love?

_____
_____
_____
_____
_____
_____
_____
_____

sixth, Contrition

Today, what choices have been inadequate responses to your love?

_____
_____
_____
_____
_____

seventh, Hope

Lord, let me look with longing toward the future. How will I let you lead me to a brighter tomorrow?

_____
_____
_____
_____
_____

Weekly *Prayer*

Anima Christi

Soul of Christ, *sanctify me.*
Body of Christ, *save me.*
Blood of Christ, *inebriate me.*
Water from the side of Christ, *wash me.*
Passion of Christ, *strengthen me.*
O Good Jesus, *hear me.*
Within your wounds, *hide me.*
Permit me not to be separated from you.
From the wicked foe, *defend me.*
At the hour of my death, *call me*
And bid me come to you,
That with your saints I may praise you
Forever and ever.
Amen.

Prayer Goals

Prayer Intentions

For whom or what do you want to pray this week? In particular, consider praying for those who frustrate or anger you, maybe even those who have harmed you or your loved ones.

_____
_____
_____
_____
_____
_____

As St. (Mother) Teresa said, "Not all of us can do great things. But we can do ... *small things with great love*"

List your "small things" below:

_____
_____
_____
_____
_____
_____
_____
_____
_____
_____

Goals Checklist

Don't feel like you need to check all these boxes every week. Start with a goal of perhaps 2 or 3 and build from there.

- [ ] Daily Mass
- [ ] Confession
- [ ] Daily Rosary
- [ ] Daily Readings
- [ ] Divine Mercy Chaplet
- [ ] Novena
- [ ] Volunteer at Homeless Shelter or Food Bank (or other Corporal Work of Mercy)
- [ ] Morning Offering
- [ ] Evening Prayer or Liturgy of the Hours
- [ ] Fasting
- [ ] Read a Saint Biography
- [ ] Angelus
- [ ] Give alms or a donation

first, Breathe

Breathe in ...
7 seconds.
Hold your breath ...
7 seconds.
Breathe out ...
7 seconds.

Repeat.

As many times
as you like.

second, Become aware of God's Presence

third, Thanksgiving

Lord, I realize that all, even myself, is a gift from you. Today, for what things am I most grateful?

fourth, Reflect

"Peace is experienced by the one who allows himself to be loved."
– Chiara Corbella Petrillo, Servant of God

fifth, Examination

Lord, open my eyes and ears to be more honest with myself. Show me what has been happening to me and in me this day. Today, how have I experienced your love?

_____
_____
_____
_____
_____
_____
_____
_____
_____
_____

sixth, Contrition

Today, what choices have been inadequate responses to your love?

_____
_____
_____
_____
_____
_____
_____

seventh, Hope

Lord, let me look with longing toward the future. How will I let you lead me to a brighter tomorrow?

_____
_____
_____
_____
_____
_____
_____

Weekly
Prayer

A Prayer for Hope

Dear Lord,
I am your humble servant and
I kneel before You today,
Helpless and weak.
I need Your hope for love,
Kindness and for a better life, Lord.
I ask that You fill me from head to toe
With Your everlasting light.
Bathe me in Your glory, Lord,
And show me that everything is
According to Your plan.
Help me walk in Your glorious light and
Show me the path,
So that I may follow You in faith.
Amen.

Prayer Goals

Prayer Intentions

For whom or what do you want to pray this week? In particular, consider praying for those who frustrate or anger you, maybe even those who have harmed you or your loved ones.

_____
_____
_____
_____
_____
_____
_____
_____
_____

As St. (Mother) Teresa said, "Not all of us can do great things. But we can do ... *small things with great love*"

List your "small things" below:

_____
_____
_____
_____
_____
_____
_____
_____
_____
_____
_____

Goals Checklist

Don't feel like you need to check all these boxes every week. Start with a goal of perhaps 2 or 3 and build from there.

- [ ] Daily Mass
- [ ] Confession
- [ ] Daily Rosary
- [ ] Daily Readings
- [ ] Divine Mercy Chaplet
- [ ] Novena
- [ ] Volunteer at Homeless Shelter or Food Bank (or other Corporal Work of Mercy)
- [ ] Morning Offering
- [ ] Evening Prayer or Liturgy of the Hours
- [ ] Fasting
- [ ] Read a Saint Biography
- [ ] Angelus
- [ ] Give alms or a donation

first, Breathe

Breathe in ...
7 seconds.
Hold your breath ...
7 seconds.
Breathe out ...
7 seconds.

Repeat.

As many times
as you like.

third, Thanksgiving

Lord, I realize that all, even myself, is a gift from you. Today, for what things am I most grateful?

second, Become aware of God's Presence

"Watch, O Lord, with those who wake or watch or weep tonight, and give your angels and saints charge over those who sleep. Tend your sick ones, O Lord Christ. Rest your weary ones. Bless your dying ones. Soothe your suffering ones. Pity your afflicted ones, shield your joyous ones. And all for love's sake."
St. Augustine of Hippo

fifth,
Examination

Lord, open my eyes and ears to be more honest with myself. Show me what has been happening to me and in me this day. Today, how have I experienced your love?

sixth
Contrition

Today, what choices have been inadequate responses to your love?

seventh,
Hope

Lord, let me look with longing toward the future. How will I let you lead me to a brighter tomorrow?

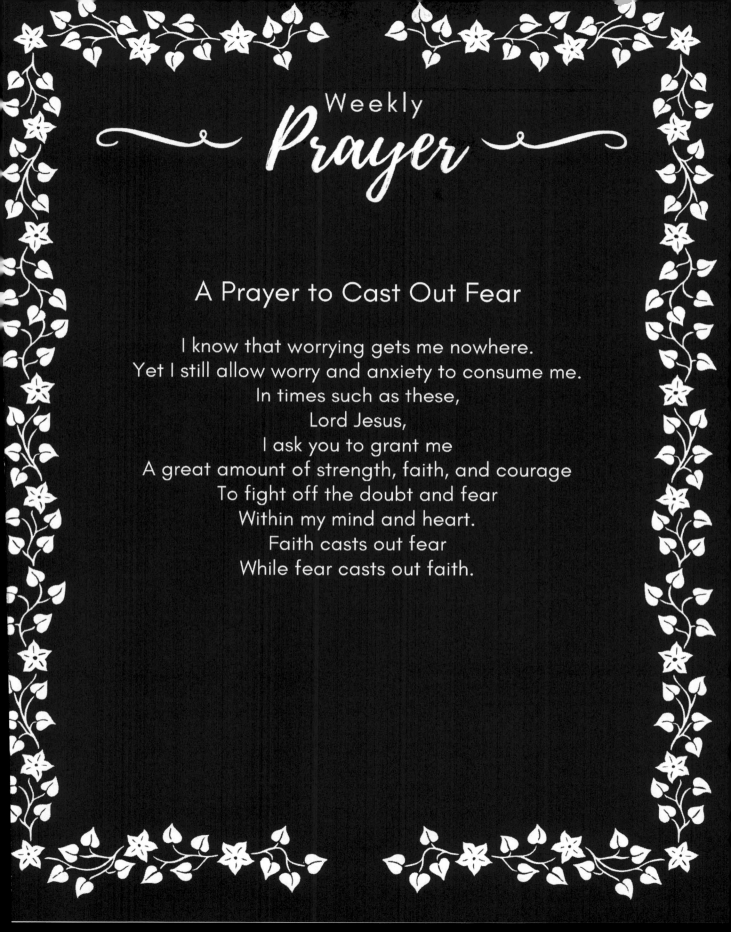

Weekly
Prayer

A Prayer to Cast Out Fear

I know that worrying gets me nowhere.
Yet I still allow worry and anxiety to consume me.
In times such as these,
Lord Jesus,
I ask you to grant me
A great amount of strength, faith, and courage
To fight off the doubt and fear
Within my mind and heart.
Faith casts out fear
While fear casts out faith.

Prayer Goals

Prayer Intentions

For whom or what do you want to pray this week? In particular, consider praying for those who frustrate or anger you, maybe even those who have harmed you or your loved ones.

_____
_____
_____
_____
_____
_____
_____
_____
_____

As St. (Mother) Teresa said, "Not all of us can do great things. But we can do ...
small things with great love"

List your "small things" below:

Goals Checklist

Don't feel like you need to check all these boxes every week. Start with a goal of perhaps 2 or 3 and build from there.

- ☐ Daily Mass
- ☐ Confession
- ☐ Daily Rosary
- ☐ Daily Readings
- ☐ Divine Mercy Chaplet
- ☐ Novena
- ☐ Volunteer at Homeless Shelter or Food Bank (or other Corporal Work of Mercy)
- ☐ Morning Offering
- ☐ Evening Prayer or Liturgy of the Hours
- ☐ Fasting
- ☐ Read a Saint Biography
- ☐ Angelus
- ☐ Give alms or a donation

_____
_____
_____
_____
_____
_____
_____
_____
_____
_____

first, Breathe

Breathe in ...
7 seconds.
Hold your breath ...
7 seconds.
Breathe out ...
7 seconds.

Repeat.

As many times
as you like.

second, Become aware of God's Presence

third, Thanksgiving

Lord, I realize that all, even myself, is a gift from you. Today, for what things am I most grateful?

"Trust and trust alone should lead us to love."
– St. Thérèse of Lisieux

fifth,
Examination

Lord, open my eyes and ears to be more honest with myself. Show me what has been happening to me and in me this day. Today, how have I experienced your love?

_____
_____
_____
_____
_____
_____
_____
_____
_____
_____

sixth
Contrition

Today, what choices have been inadequate responses to your love?

_____
_____
_____
_____
_____

seventh,
Hope

Lord, let me look with longing toward the future. How will I let you lead me to a brighter tomorrow?

_____
_____
_____
_____
_____

Weekly Prayer

Memorare

Remember,
Most loving Virgin Mary,
Never was it heard that
Anyone who turned to you for help
Was left unaided.

Inspired by this confidence,
Though burdened by my sins,
I run to your protection
For you are my mother.

Mother of the Word of God,
Do not despise my words of pleading
But be merciful and hear my prayer.
Amen.

Prayer Goals

Prayer Intentions

For whom or what do you want to pray this week? In particular, consider praying for those who frustrate or anger you, maybe even those who have harmed you or your loved ones.

_____
_____
_____
_____
_____
_____
_____
_____
_____
_____

As St. (Mother) Teresa said, "Not all of us can do great things. But we can do ... *small things with great love*"

List your "small things" below:

_____
_____
_____
_____
_____
_____
_____
_____
_____
_____
_____

Goals Checklist

Don't feel like you need to check all these boxes every week. Start with a goal of perhaps 2 or 3 and build from there.

- [ ] Daily Mass
- [ ] Confession
- [ ] Daily Rosary
- [ ] Daily Readings
- [ ] Divine Mercy Chaplet
- [ ] Novena
- [ ] Volunteer at Homeless Shelter or Food Bank (or other Corporal Work of Mercy)

- [ ] Morning Offering
- [ ] Evening Prayer or Liturgy of the Hours
- [ ] Fasting
- [ ] Read a Saint Biography
- [ ] Angelus
- [ ] Give alms or a donation

first, Breathe

Breathe in ...
7 seconds.
Hold your breath ...
7 seconds.
Breathe out ...
7 seconds.

Repeat.

As many times
as you like.

second, Become aware of God's Presence

third, Thanksgiving

Lord, I realize that all, even myself, is a gift from you. Today, for what things am I most grateful?

fourth, Reflect

"And do not fear those who kill the body but cannot kill the soul; rather fear him who can destroy both soul and body in hell. Are not two sparrows sold for a penny? And not one of them will fall to the ground without your Father's will. But even the hairs of your head are all numbered.
Fear not, therefore; you are of more value than many sparrows."
Matthew 10:28–31

fifth, Examination

Lord, open my eyes and ears to be more honest with myself. Show me what has been happening to me and in me this day. Today, how have I experienced your love?

_____
_____
_____
_____
_____
_____
_____
_____
_____
_____
_____
_____

sixth, Contrition

Today, what choices have been inadequate responses to your love?

_____
_____
_____
_____
_____
_____

seventh, Hope

Lord, let me look with longing toward the future. How will I let you lead me to a brighter tomorrow?

_____
_____
_____
_____
_____
_____

Weekly
Prayer

A Prayer for Letting Go of Worries

Heavenly Father,
Lately I've been so worried about
Things that are out of my control.
Help me to trust that
You are working out
Every little detail of my life and
That I have nothing to fear
Or worry about.
In Jesus' name,
Amen.

Prayer Goals

Prayer Intentions

For whom or what do you want to pray this week? In particular, consider praying for those who frustrate or anger you, maybe even those who have harmed you or your loved ones.

_____
_____
_____
_____
_____
_____
_____
_____

As St. (Mother) Teresa said, "Not all of us can do great things. But we can do ... *small things with great love*"

List your "small things" below:

_____
_____
_____
_____
_____
_____
_____
_____
_____
_____

Goals Checklist

Don't feel like you need to check all these boxes every week. Start with a goal of perhaps 2 or 3 and build from there.

- ☐ Daily Mass
- ☐ Confession
- ☐ Daily Rosary
- ☐ Daily Readings
- ☐ Divine Mercy Chaplet
- ☐ Novena
- ☐ Volunteer at Homeless Shelter or Food Bank (or other Corporal Work of Mercy)
- ☐ Morning Offering
- ☐ Evening Prayer or Liturgy of the Hours
- ☐ Fasting
- ☐ Read a Saint Biography
- ☐ Angelus
- ☐ Give alms or a donation

first, Breathe ...

Breathe in ...
7 seconds.
Hold your breath ...
7 seconds.
Breathe out ...
7 seconds.

Repeat.

As many times
as you like.

second, Become aware of God's Presence

third, Thanksgiving

Lord, I realize that all, even myself, is a gift from you. Today, for what things am I most grateful?

"And of what should we be afraid? Our captain on this battlefield is Christ Jesus. We have discovered what we have to do. Christ has bound our enemies for us and weakened them that they cannot overcome us unless we so choose to let them. So we must fight courageously and mark ourselves with the sign of the most Holy Cross."
– St. Catherine of Siena

fifth,
Examination

Lord, open my eyes and ears to be more honest with myself. Show me what has been happening to me and in me this day. Today, how have I experienced your love?

_____
_____
_____
_____
_____
_____
_____
_____
_____
_____
_____
_____

sixth
Contrition

Today, what choices have been inadequate responses to your love?

_____
_____
_____
_____
_____
_____
_____

seventh,
Hope

Lord, let me look with longing toward the future. How will I let you lead me to a brighter tomorrow?

_____
_____
_____
_____
_____
_____
_____

Weekly
Prayer

Magnificat

My soul proclaims the greatness of the Lord,
My spirit rejoices in God my Savior;
For he has looked with favor on his lowly servant.
From this day all generations will call me blessed:
The Almighty has done great things for me,
And holy is his Name.
He has mercy on those who fear him
in every generation.
He has shown the strength of his arm,
He has scattered the proud in their conceit.
He has cast down the mighty from their thrones,
And has lifted up the lowly.
He has filled the hungry with good things,
And the rich he has sent away empty.
He has come to the help of his servant Israel
For he has remembered his promise of mercy,
The promise he made to our fathers,
To Abraham and his children forever.

Prayer Goals

Prayer Intentions

For whom or what do you want to pray this week? In particular, consider praying for those who frustrate or anger you, maybe even those who have harmed you or your loved ones.

_____

_____

_____

_____

_____

_____

_____

_____

As St. (Mother) Teresa said, "Not all of us can do great things. But we can do ... *small things with great love*"

List your "small things" below:

_____

_____

_____

_____

_____

_____

_____

_____

_____

_____

_____

Goals Checklist

Don't feel like you need to check all these boxes every week. Start with a goal of perhaps 2 or 3 and build from there.

- [ ] Daily Mass
- [ ] Confession
- [ ] Daily Rosary
- [ ] Daily Readings
- [ ] Divine Mercy Chaplet
- [ ] Novena
- [ ] Volunteer at Homeless Shelter or Food Bank (or other Corporal Work of Mercy)
- [ ] Morning Offering
- [ ] Evening Prayer or Liturgy of the Hours
- [ ] Fasting
- [ ] Read a Saint Biography
- [ ] Angelus
- [ ] Give alms or a donation

first, Breathe

Breathe in ...
7 seconds.
Hold your breath ...
7 seconds.
Breathe out ...
7 seconds.

Repeat.

As many times
as you like.

second, Become aware of God's Presence

third, Thanksgiving

Lord, I realize that all, even myself, is a gift from you. Today, for what things am I most grateful?

"If certain thoughts bother you, it is devil who causes you to worry, and not God, Who, being the spirit of peace, grants you tranquility."
– St. (Padre) Pio of Pietrelcina

fifth, Examination

Lord, open my eyes and ears to be more honest with myself. Show me what has been happening to me and in me this day. Today, how have I experienced your love?

_____

_____

_____

_____

_____

_____

_____

_____

_____

_____

sixth Contrition

Today, what choices have been inadequate responses to your love?

_____

_____

_____

_____

_____

seventh, Hope

Lord, let me look with longing toward the future. How will I let you lead me to a brighter tomorrow?

_____

_____

_____

_____

_____

Weekly
Prayer

A Prayer for Unburdening the Mind

Dear Loving Lord,
I am feeling stress, I am worried.
Too many things occupy my mind.
Won't you help me?
Show me, Lord,
Your order and Your plans are eternal.
Let me trust in Your Will alone.
Your Word tells me where there is love,
there is no fear.
Let me be filled with Your Love.
The perfect love
That tells me I am not condemned,
but I am saved.
I can do all things through You.
You strengthen me.
In Jesus name,
Amen.

Prayer Goals

Prayer Intentions

For whom or what do you want to pray this week? In particular, consider praying for those who frustrate or anger you, maybe even those who have harmed you or your loved ones.

_____
_____
_____
_____
_____
_____
_____
_____

As St. (Mother) Teresa said, "Not all of us can do great things. But we can do ... *small things with great love*"

List your "small things" below:

_____
_____
_____
_____
_____
_____
_____
_____
_____

Goals Checklist

Don't feel like you need to check all these boxes every week. Start with a goal of perhaps 2 or 3 and build from there.

- ☐ Daily Mass
- ☐ Confession
- ☐ Daily Rosary
- ☐ Daily Readings
- ☐ Divine Mercy Chaplet
- ☐ Novena
- ☐ Volunteer at Homeless Shelter or Food Bank
  (or other Corporal Work of Mercy)
- ☐ Morning Offering
- ☐ Evening Prayer or Liturgy of the Hours
- ☐ Fasting
- ☐ Read a Saint Biography
- ☐ Angelus
- ☐ Give alms or a donation

first, Breathe

Breathe in ...
7 seconds.
Hold your breath ...
7 seconds.
Breathe out ...
7 seconds.

Repeat.

As many times
as you like.

second, Become aware of God's Presence

third, Thanksgiving

Lord, I realize that all, even myself, is a gift from you. Today, for what things am I most grateful?

fourth, Reflect

"In sorrow and suffering, go straight to God with confidence, and you will be strengthened, enlightened, and instructed."
– St. John of the Cross

fifth, Examination

Lord, open my eyes and ears to be more honest with myself. Show me what has been happening to me and in me this day. Today, how have I experienced your love?

_____
_____
_____
_____
_____
_____
_____
_____
_____
_____
_____

sixth, Contrition

Today, what choices have been inadequate responses to your love?

_____
_____
_____
_____
_____

seventh, Hope

Lord, let me look with longing toward the future. How will I let you lead me to a brighter tomorrow?

_____
_____
_____
_____
_____

Weekly *Prayer*

St. Francis' Canticle of the Sun

Be praised, my Lord,
For all your creatures,
And first for brother sun,
Who makes the day bright and luminous.
He is beautiful and radiant
With great splendor
He is the image of You,
Most high.
Be praised, my Lord,
For sister moon and the stars.
You placed them in the sky,
So bright and twinkling.

Prayer Goals

Prayer Intentions

For whom or what do you want to pray this week? In particular, consider praying for those who frustrate or anger you, maybe even those who have harmed you or your loved ones.

_____
_____
_____
_____
_____
_____
_____
_____
_____

As St. (Mother) Teresa said, "Not all of us can do great things. But we can do ... *small things with great love*"

List your "small things" below:

_____
_____
_____
_____
_____
_____
_____
_____
_____
_____
_____

Goals Checklist

Don't feel like you need to check all these boxes every week. Start with a goal of perhaps 2 or 3 and build from there.

- [ ] Daily Mass
- [ ] Confession
- [ ] Daily Rosary
- [ ] Daily Readings
- [ ] Divine Mercy Chaplet
- [ ] Novena
- [ ] Volunteer at Homeless Shelter or Food Bank
  (or other Corporal Work of Mercy)

- [ ] Morning Offering
- [ ] Evening Prayer or Liturgy of the Hours
- [ ] Fasting
- [ ] Read a Saint Biography
- [ ] Angelus
- [ ] Give alms or a donation

first, Breathe

Breathe in ...
7 seconds.
Hold your breath ...
7 seconds.
Breathe out ...
7 seconds.

Repeat.

As many times
as you like.

second, Become aware of God's Presence

third, Thanksgiving

Lord, I realize that all, even myself, is a gift from you. Today, for what things am I most grateful?

fourth, Reflect

"Yesterday is gone. Tomorrow has not yet come.
We only have today. Let us begin."
– St. (Mother) Teresa of Calcutta

fifth, Examination

Lord, open my eyes and ears to be more honest with myself. Show me what has been happening to me and in me this day. Today, how have I experienced your love?

_____
_____
_____
_____
_____
_____
_____
_____
_____
_____
_____

sixth, Contrition

Today, what choices have been inadequate responses to your love?

_____
_____
_____
_____
_____
_____
_____

seventh, Hope

Lord, let me look with longing toward the future. How will I let you lead me to a brighter tomorrow?

_____
_____
_____
_____
_____
_____
_____

Weekly
Prayer

A Celtic Prayer of Peace
David Adam

Calm me, Lord, as you calmed the storm;
Still me, Lord, keep me from harm.

Let all the tumult within me cease,
Enfold me, Lord, in your peace.

Calm me, Lord, as you calmed the storm;
Still me, Lord, keep me from harm.

Let all the tumult within me cease, Lord,
Enfold me in your peace.

Prayer Goals

Prayer Intentions

For whom or what do you want to pray this week? In particular, consider praying for those who frustrate or anger you, maybe even those who have harmed you or your loved ones.

_____
_____
_____
_____
_____
_____
_____
_____
_____
_____

As St. (Mother) Teresa said, "Not all of us can do great things. But we can do ... *small things with great love*"

List your "small things" below:

_____
_____
_____
_____
_____
_____
_____
_____
_____
_____
_____

Goals Checklist

Don't feel like you need to check all these boxes every week. Start with a goal of perhaps 2 or 3 and build from there.

- [ ] Daily Mass
- [ ] Confession
- [ ] Daily Rosary
- [ ] Daily Readings
- [ ] Divine Mercy Chaplet
- [ ] Novena
- [ ] Volunteer at Homeless Shelter or Food Bank (or other Corporal Work of Mercy)
- [ ] Morning Offering
- [ ] Evening Prayer or Liturgy of the Hours
- [ ] Fasting
- [ ] Read a Saint Biography
- [ ] Angelus
- [ ] Give alms or a donation

first, Breathe

Breathe in ...
7 seconds.
Hold your breath ...
7 seconds.
Breathe out ...
7 seconds.

Repeat.

As many times
as you like.

second, Become aware of God's Presence

third, Thanksgiving

Lord, I realize that all, even myself, is a gift from you. Today, for what things am I most grateful?

fourth, Reflect

"Seen from the outside, all these trials are frightening.
We wondered if we could ever confront anything similar.
But each step is accompanied by a necessary grace."
– Chiara Corbella Petrillo, Servant of God

fifth, Examination

Lord, open my eyes and ears to be more honest with myself. Show me what has been happening to me and in me this day. Today, how have I experienced your love?

_____
_____
_____
_____
_____
_____
_____
_____

sixth Contrition

Today, what choices have been inadequate responses to your love?

_____
_____
_____
_____
_____

seventh, Hope

Lord, let me look with longing toward the future. How will I let you lead me to a brighter tomorrow?

_____
_____
_____
_____
_____

Weekly *Prayer*

Prayer of Saint Richard of Chichester

Thanks be to thee,
My Lord Jesus Christ,
For all the benefits Thou hast given me,
For all the pains and insults
Thou hast borne for me.
O most merciful redeemer,
Friend and Brother,
May I know Thee more clearly,
Love Thee more dearly, and
Follow Thee more nearly,
Day by day.
Amen.

Prayer Goals

Prayer Intentions

For whom or what do you want to pray this week? In particular, consider praying for those who frustrate or anger you, maybe even those who have harmed you or your loved ones.

_____
_____
_____
_____
_____
_____
_____
_____
_____

As St. (Mother) Teresa said, "Not all of us can do great things. But we can do ...

small things with great love"

List your "small things" below:

_____
_____
_____
_____
_____
_____
_____
_____
_____
_____
_____
_____

Goals Checklist

Don't feel like you need to check all these boxes every week. Start with a goal of perhaps 2 or 3 and build from there.

- ☐ Daily Mass
- ☐ Confession
- ☐ Daily Rosary
- ☐ Daily Readings
- ☐ Divine Mercy Chaplet
- ☐ Novena
- ☐ Volunteer at Homeless Shelter or Food Bank (or other Corporal Work of Mercy)
- ☐ Morning Offering
- ☐ Evening Prayer or Liturgy of the Hours
- ☐ Fasting
- ☐ Read a Saint Biography
- ☐ Angelus
- ☐ Give alms or a donation

first, Breathe

Breathe in ...
7 seconds.
Hold your breath ...
7 seconds.
Breathe out ...
7 seconds.

Repeat.

As many times
as you like.

second, Become aware of God's Presence

third, Thanksgiving

Lord, I realize that all, even myself, is a gift from you. Today, for what things am I most grateful?

"Peace be with you. This is not a greeting nor even a simple good wish: it is a gift, indeed, the precious gift that Christ offered His disciples after he had passed through death and hell."
– Pope Francis

fifth, Examination

Lord, open my eyes and ears to be more honest with myself. Show me what has been happening to me and in me this day. Today, how have I experienced your love?

_____
_____
_____
_____
_____
_____
_____
_____
_____
_____
_____
_____

sixth Contrition

Today, what choices have been inadequate responses to your love?

_____
_____
_____
_____
_____
_____
_____
_____
_____

seventh, Hope

Lord, let me look with longing toward the future. How will I let you lead me to a brighter tomorrow?

_____
_____
_____
_____
_____
_____
_____
_____
_____

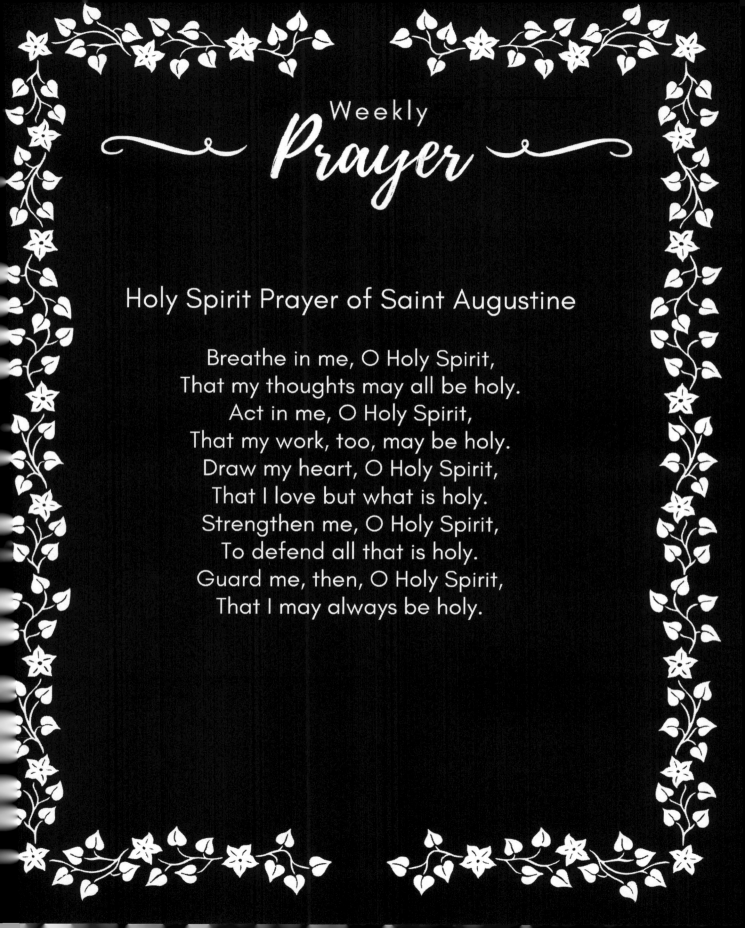

Weekly
Prayer

Holy Spirit Prayer of Saint Augustine

Breathe in me, O Holy Spirit,
That my thoughts may all be holy.
Act in me, O Holy Spirit,
That my work, too, may be holy.
Draw my heart, O Holy Spirit,
That I love but what is holy.
Strengthen me, O Holy Spirit,
To defend all that is holy.
Guard me, then, O Holy Spirit,
That I may always be holy.

Prayer Goals

Prayer Intentions

For whom or what do you want to pray this week? In particular, consider praying for those who frustrate or anger you, maybe even those who have harmed you or your loved ones.

_____
_____
_____
_____
_____
_____
_____
_____
_____
_____
_____

As St. (Mother) Teresa said, "Not all of us can do great things. But we can do ... *small things with great love*"

List your "small things" below:

_____
_____
_____
_____
_____
_____
_____
_____
_____
_____
_____

Goals Checklist

Don't feel like you need to check all these boxes every week. Start with a goal of perhaps 2 or 3 and build from there.

- [ ] Daily Mass
- [ ] Confession
- [ ] Daily Rosary
- [ ] Daily Readings
- [ ] Divine Mercy Chaplet
- [ ] Novena
- [ ] Volunteer at Homeless Shelter or Food Bank (or other Corporal Work of Mercy)
- [ ] Morning Offering
- [ ] Evening Prayer or Liturgy of the Hours
- [ ] Fasting
- [ ] Read a Saint Biography
- [ ] Angelus
- [ ] Give alms or a donation

first, Breathe

Breathe in …
7 seconds.
Hold your breath …
7 seconds.
Breathe out …
7 seconds.

Repeat.

As many times
as you like.

second, Become aware of God's Presence

third, Thanksgiving

Lord, I realize that all, even myself, is a gift from you. Today, for what things am I most grateful?

The Lord is my shepherd, I shall not want; He makes me lie down in green pastures. He leads me beside still waters; He restores my soul. He leads me in paths of righteousness for His name's sake.
Psalm 23:1-3

fifth,
Examination

Lord, open my eyes and ears to be more honest with myself. Show me what has been happening to me and in me this day. Today, how have I experienced your love?

sixth,
Contrition

Today, what choices have been inadequate responses to your love?

seventh,
Hope

Lord, let me look with longing toward the future. How will I let you lead me to a brighter tomorrow?

Weekly
Prayer

~ ◡ ~

"Take and Receive" Prayer

Take, Lord, and receive all my liberty,
My memory, my understanding,
And my entire will –
All that I have and call my own.
You have given it all to me.
To you, Lord, I return it.
Everything is yours;
Do with it what you will.
Give me only your love and your grace.
That is enough for me.
Amen.

Prayer Goals

Prayer Intentions

For whom or what do you want to pray this week? In particular, consider praying for those who frustrate or anger you, maybe even those who have harmed you or your loved ones.

_____

_____

_____

_____

_____

_____

_____

_____

_____

As St. (Mother) Teresa said, "Not all of us can do great things. But we can do ... *small things with great love*"

List your "small things" below:

_____

_____

_____

_____

_____

_____

_____

_____

_____

_____

Goals Checklist

Don't feel like you need to check all these boxes every week. Start with a goal of perhaps 2 or 3 and build from there.

- [ ] Daily Mass
- [ ] Confession
- [ ] Daily Rosary
- [ ] Daily Readings
- [ ] Divine Mercy Chaplet
- [ ] Novena
- [ ] Volunteer at Homeless Shelter or Food Bank (or other Corporal Work of Mercy)
- [ ] Morning Offering
- [ ] Evening Prayer or Liturgy of the Hours
- [ ] Fasting
- [ ] Read a Saint Biography
- [ ] Angelus
- [ ] Give alms or a donation

Week Twenty-Eight

first, Breathe

Breathe in ...
7 seconds.
Hold your breath ...
7 seconds.
Breathe out ...
7 seconds.

Repeat.

As many times
as you like.

second, Become aware of God's Presence

third, Thanksgiving

Lord, I realize that all, even myself, is a gift from you. Today, for what things am I most grateful?

Reflect

Even though I walk through the valley of the shadow of death, I fear no evil;
for Thou art with me; thy rod and thy staff, they comfort me.
Psalm 23:4

fifth,
Examination

Lord, open my eyes and ears to be more honest with myself. Show me what has been happening to me and in me this day. Today, how have I experienced your love?

_____
_____
_____
_____
_____
_____
_____
_____
_____
_____
_____
_____
_____

sixth,
Contrition

Today, what choices have been inadequate responses to your love?

_____
_____
_____
_____
_____
_____

seventh,
Hope

Lord, let me look with longing toward the future. How will I let you lead me to a brighter tomorrow?

_____
_____
_____
_____
_____
_____

Weekly
Prayer

Act of Hope

My God, relying on your
infinite goodness and promises,
I hope to obtain pardon of my sins,
Help of your grace,
And life everlasting
Through the merits of Jesus Christ,
My Lord and Redeemer
Amen.

Prayer Goals

Prayer Intentions

For whom or what do you want to pray this week? In particular, consider praying for those who frustrate or anger you, maybe even those who have harmed you or your loved ones.

_____
_____
_____
_____
_____
_____
_____
_____

As St. (Mother) Teresa said, "Not all of us can do great things. But we can do ... *small things with great love*"

List your "small things" below:

_____
_____
_____
_____
_____
_____
_____
_____
_____
_____

Goals Checklist

Don't feel like you need to check all these boxes every week. Start with a goal of perhaps 2 or 3 and build from there.

- [ ] Daily Mass
- [ ] Confession
- [ ] Daily Rosary
- [ ] Daily Readings
- [ ] Divine Mercy Chaplet
- [ ] Novena
- [ ] Volunteer at Homeless Shelter or Food Bank (or other Corporal Work of Mercy)
- [ ] Morning Offering
- [ ] Evening Prayer or Liturgy of the Hours
- [ ] Fasting
- [ ] Read a Saint Biography
- [ ] Angelus
- [ ] Give alms or a donation

first, Breathe

Breathe in ...
7 seconds.
Hold your breath ...
7 seconds.
Breathe out ...
7 seconds.

Repeat.

As many times
as you like.

second,
Become aware of
God's Presence

third,
Thanksgiving

Lord, I realize that all, even myself, is a gift from you. Today, for what things am I most grateful?

fourth, Reflect

"Our hearts were made for You, O Lord,
and they are restless until they rest in You."
St. Augustine of Hippo

fifth, Examination

Lord, open my eyes and ears to be more honest with myself. Show me what has been happening to me and in me this day. Today, how have I experienced your love?

sixth, Contrition

Today, what choices have been inadequate responses to your love?

seventh, Hope

Lord, let me look with longing toward the future. How will I let you lead me to a brighter tomorrow?

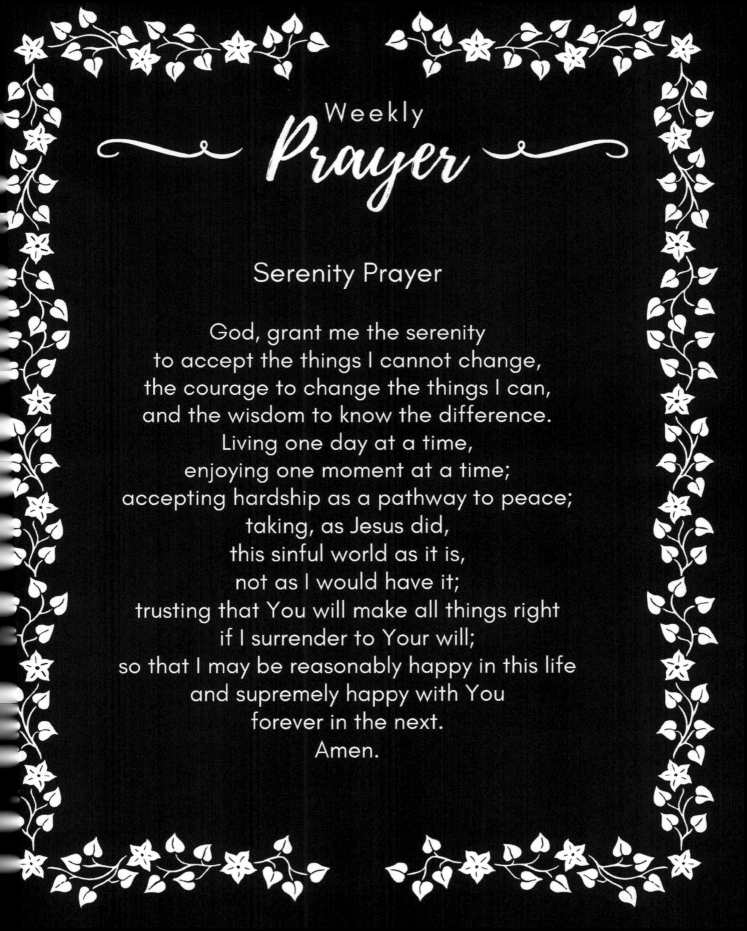

Weekly
Prayer

Serenity Prayer

God, grant me the serenity
to accept the things I cannot change,
the courage to change the things I can,
and the wisdom to know the difference.
Living one day at a time,
enjoying one moment at a time;
accepting hardship as a pathway to peace;
taking, as Jesus did,
this sinful world as it is,
not as I would have it;
trusting that You will make all things right
if I surrender to Your will;
so that I may be reasonably happy in this life
and supremely happy with You
forever in the next.
Amen.

Prayer Goals

Prayer Intentions

For whom or what do you want to pray this week? In particular, consider praying for those who frustrate or anger you, maybe even those who have harmed you or your loved ones.

_____
_____
_____
_____
_____
_____
_____
_____

As St. (Mother) Teresa said, "Not all of us can do great things. But we can do ... *small things with great love*"

List your "small things" below:

_____
_____
_____
_____
_____
_____
_____
_____
_____
_____

Goals Checklist

Don't feel like you need to check all these boxes every week. Start with a goal of perhaps 2 or 3 and build from there.

- [ ] Daily Mass
- [ ] Confession
- [ ] Daily Rosary
- [ ] Daily Readings
- [ ] Divine Mercy Chaplet
- [ ] Novena
- [ ] Volunteer at Homeless Shelter or Food Bank
  (or other Corporal Work of Mercy)

- [ ] Morning Offering
- [ ] Evening Prayer or Liturgy of the Hours
- [ ] Fasting
- [ ] Read a Saint Biography
- [ ] Angelus
- [ ] Give alms or a donation

first, Breathe

Breathe in ...
7 seconds.
Hold your breath ...
7 seconds.
Breathe out ...
7 seconds.

Repeat.

As many times
as you like.

second, Become aware of God's Presence

third, Thanksgiving

Lord, I realize that all, even myself, is a gift from you. Today, for what things am I most grateful?

"Fear not, I am with you; be not dismayed; I am your God. I will strengthen you, and help you, and uphold you with my right hand of justice."
Isaiah 41:10

fifth,
Examination

Lord, open my eyes and ears to be more honest with myself. Show me what has been happening to me and in me this day. Today, how have I experienced your love?

_____
_____
_____
_____
_____
_____
_____
_____
_____
_____
_____

sixth,
Contrition

Today, what choices have been inadequate responses to your love?

_____
_____
_____
_____
_____
_____

seventh,
Hope

Lord, let me look with longing toward the future. How will I let you lead me to a brighter tomorrow?

_____
_____
_____
_____
_____
_____

Weekly *Prayer*

Litany of Humility

O Jesus, meek and humble of heart, *Hear me.*
From the desire of being esteemed, *Deliver me, O Jesus.*
From the desire of being loved, *Deliver me, O Jesus.*
From the desire of being extolled, *Deliver me, O Jesus.*
From the desire of being honored, *Deliver me, O Jesus.*
From the desire of being praised, *Deliver me, O Jesus.*
From the desire of being preferred to others, *Deliver me, O Jesus.*
From the desire of being consulted, *Deliver me, O Jesus.*
From the desire of being approved, *Deliver me, O Jesus.*
From the fear of being humiliated, *Deliver me, O Jesus.*
From the fear of being despised, *Deliver me, O Jesus.*
From the fear of suffering rebukes, *Deliver me, O Jesus.*
From the fear of being calumniated, *Deliver me, O Jesus.*
From the fear of being forgotten, *Deliver me, O Jesus.*
From the fear of being ridiculed, *Deliver me, O Jesus.*
From the fear of being wronged, *Deliver me, O Jesus.*
From the fear of being suspected, *Deliver me, O Jesus.*
That others may be loved more than I,
Jesus, grant me the grace to desire it.
That others may be esteemed more than I,
Jesus, grant me the grace to desire it.
That, in the opinion of the world, others may increase and I may decrease,
Jesus, grant me the grace to desire it.
That others may be chosen and I set aside,
Jesus, grant me the grace to desire it.
That others may be praised and I go unnoticed,
Jesus, grant me the grace to desire it.
That others may be preferred to me in everything,
Jesus, grant me the grace to desire it.
That others may become holier than I, provided that I may become as holy as I
should, *Jesus, grant me the grace to desire it.*
Amen.

Prayer Goals

Prayer Intentions

For whom or what do you want to pray this week? In particular, consider praying for those who frustrate or anger you, maybe even those who have harmed you or your loved ones.

_____
_____
_____
_____
_____
_____
_____

As St. (Mother) Teresa said, "Not all of us can do great things. But we can do ... *small things with great love*"

List your "small things" below:

_____
_____
_____
_____
_____
_____
_____
_____
_____
_____
_____

Goals Checklist

Don't feel like you need to check all these boxes every week. Start with a goal of perhaps 2 or 3 and build from there.

- ☐ Daily Mass
- ☐ Confession
- ☐ Daily Rosary
- ☐ Daily Readings
- ☐ Divine Mercy Chaplet
- ☐ Novena
- ☐ Volunteer at Homeless Shelter or Food Bank (or other Corporal Work of Mercy)
- ☐ Morning Offering
- ☐ Evening Prayer or Liturgy of the Hours
- ☐ Fasting
- ☐ Read a Saint Biography
- ☐ Angelus
- ☐ Give alms or a donation

Week Thirty-One

first, Breathe

Breathe in ...
7 seconds.
Hold your breath ...
7 seconds.
Breathe out ...
7 seconds.

Repeat.

As many times
as you like.

second, Become aware of God's Presence

third, Thanksgiving

Lord, I realize that all, even myself, is a gift from you. Today, for what things am I most grateful?

fourth, Reflect

"Be patient because the weaknesses of the body are given to us in this world
by God for the salvation of the soul,
so they are of great merit when they are borne patiently."
– St. Francis of Assisi

fifth, Examination

Lord, open my eyes and ears to be more honest with myself. Show me what has been happening to me and in me this day. Today, how have I experienced your love?

_____
_____
_____
_____
_____
_____
_____
_____
_____
_____
_____

sixth, Contrition

Today, what choices have been inadequate responses to your love?

_____
_____
_____
_____
_____
_____

seventh, Hope

Lord, let me look with longing toward the future. How will I let you lead me to a brighter tomorrow?

_____
_____
_____
_____
_____
_____

Weekly
Prayer

Prayer for Calm

My Lord and my God,
I do not know what will happen to me today,
But what I do know is that
Nothing will happen to me today
That You and I together cannot handle.
This thought is enough
To bring me to face the day in peace.
I adore you in your wisdom and love.
I commend myself into your hands with the
complete trust.
Amen.

Prayer Goals

Prayer Intentions

For whom or what do you want to pray this week? In particular, consider praying for those who frustrate or anger you, maybe even those who have harmed you or your loved ones.

_____
_____
_____
_____
_____
_____
_____
_____
_____
_____

As St. (Mother) Teresa said, "Not all of us can do great things. But we can do ... *small things with great love*"

List your "small things" below:

_____
_____
_____
_____
_____
_____
_____
_____
_____
_____
_____
_____

Goals Checklist

Don't feel like you need to check all these boxes every week. Start with a goal of perhaps 2 or 3 and build from there.

- [ ] Daily Mass
- [ ] Confession
- [ ] Daily Rosary
- [ ] Daily Readings
- [ ] Divine Mercy Chaplet
- [ ] Novena
- [ ] Volunteer at Homeless Shelter or Food Bank (or other Corporal Work of Mercy)

- [ ] Morning Offering
- [ ] Evening Prayer or Liturgy of the Hours
- [ ] Fasting
- [ ] Read a Saint Biography
- [ ] Angelus
- [ ] Give alms or a donation

first, Breathe

Breathe in ...
7 seconds.
Hold your breath ...
7 seconds.
Breathe out ...
7 seconds.

Repeat.

As many times
as you like.

second, Become aware of God's Presence

third, Thanksgiving

Lord, I realize that all, even myself, is a gift from you. Today, for what things am I most grateful?

fourth,
Reflect

"A humble soul does not trust itself,
but places all its confidence in God."
– St. Maria Faustina Kowalska

fifth,
Examination

Lord, open my eyes and ears to be more honest with myself. Show me what has been happening to me and in me this day. Today, how have I experienced your love?

_____

_____

_____

_____

_____

_____

_____

_____

_____

_____

_____

sixth
Contrition

Today, what choices have been inadequate responses to your love?

seventh,
Hope

Lord, let me look with longing toward the future. How will I let you lead me to a brighter tomorrow?

_____

_____

_____

_____

_____

_____

_____

Weekly
Prayer

Litany of Trust, Part One
From the Sisters of Life

From the belief that I have to earn Your love,
Deliver me, Jesus.
From the fear that I am unlovable,
Deliver me, Jesus.
From the false security that I have what it takes,
Deliver me, Jesus.
From the fear that trusting You will leave me more destitute,
Deliver me, Jesus.
From all suspicion of Your words and promises,
Deliver me, Jesus.
From the rebellion against childlike dependency on You,
Deliver me, Jesus.
From refusals and reluctances in accepting Your will,
Deliver me, Jesus.
From anxiety about the future,
Deliver me, Jesus.
From resentment or excessive preoccupation with the past,
Deliver me, Jesus.
From restless self-seeking in the present moment,
Deliver me, Jesus.
From disbelief in Your love and presence,
Deliver me, Jesus.
From the fear of being asked to give more than I have,
Deliver me, Jesus.
From the belief that my life has no meaning or worth,
Deliver me, Jesus.
From the fear of what love demands,
Deliver me, Jesus.
From discouragement,
Deliver me. Jesus.

Prayer Goals

Prayer Intentions

For whom or what do you want to pray this week? In particular, consider praying for those who frustrate or anger you, maybe even those who have harmed you or your loved ones.

_____
_____
_____
_____
_____
_____

As St. (Mother) Teresa said, "Not all of us can do great things. But we can do ... *small things with great love*"

List your "small things" below:

_____
_____
_____
_____
_____
_____
_____
_____
_____

Goals Checklist

Don't feel like you need to check all these boxes every week. Start with a goal of perhaps 2 or 3 and build from there.

- [ ] Daily Mass
- [ ] Confession
- [ ] Daily Rosary
- [ ] Daily Readings
- [ ] Divine Mercy Chaplet
- [ ] Novena
- [ ] Volunteer at Homeless Shelter or Food Bank (or other Corporal Work of Mercy)
- [ ] Morning Offering
- [ ] Evening Prayer or Liturgy of the Hours
- [ ] Fasting
- [ ] Read a Saint Biography
- [ ] Angelus
- [ ] Give alms or a donation

first, Breathe

Breathe in ...
7 seconds.
Hold your breath ...
7 seconds.
Breathe out ...
7 seconds.

Repeat.

As many times
as you like.

second, Become aware of God's Presence

third, Thanksgiving

Lord, I realize that all, even myself, is a gift from you. Today, for what things am I most grateful?

"Therefore I tell you, do not be anxious about your life, what you shall eat or what you shall drink, nor about your body, what you shall put on. Is not life more than food, and the body more than clothing? Look at the birds of the air: they neither sow nor reap nor gather into barns, and yet your heavenly Father feeds them. Are you not of more value than they? And which of you by being anxious can add one cubit to his span of life?" (Matthew 6:25-27)

fifth, Examination

Lord, open my eyes and ears to be more honest with myself. Show me what has been happening to me and in me this day. Today, how have I experienced your love?

_____
_____
_____
_____
_____
_____
_____
_____
_____
_____

sixth, Contrition

Today, what choices have been inadequate responses to your love?

_____
_____
_____
_____
_____
_____

seventh, Hope

Lord, let me look with longing toward the future. How will I let you lead me to a brighter tomorrow?

_____
_____
_____
_____
_____
_____

Weekly
Prayer

Litany of Trust, Part Two
From the Sisters of Life

That You are continually holding me, sustaining me, loving me,
Jesus, I trust in You.
That Your love goes deeper than my sins and failings and transforms me,
Jesus, I trust in You.
That not knowing what tomorrow brings is an invitation to lean on You,
Jesus, I trust in You.
That You are with me in my suffering, *Jesus, I trust in You.*
That my suffering, united to Your own, will bear fruit in this life and the
next, *Jesus, I trust in You.*
That You will not leave me orphan, that You are present in Your Church,
Jesus, I trust in You.
That Your plan is better than anything else, *Jesus, I trust in You.*
That You always hear me and in Your goodness always respond to me
Jesus, I trust in You.
That You give me the grace to accept forgiveness and to forgive others
Jesus, I trust in You.
That You give me all the strength I need for what is asked
Jesus, I trust in You.
That my life is a gift, *Jesus, I trust in You.*
That You will teach me to trust You, *Jesus, I trust in You.*
That You are my Lord and my God, *Jesus, I trust in You.*
That I am Your beloved one, *Jesus, I trust in You.*

Prayer Goals

Prayer Intentions

For whom or what do you want to pray this week? In particular, consider praying for those who frustrate or anger you, maybe even those who have harmed you or your loved ones.

_____
_____
_____
_____
_____
_____
_____
_____

> As St. (Mother) Teresa said, "Not all of us can do great things. But we can do ... *small things with great love*"

List your "small things" below:

_____
_____
_____
_____
_____
_____
_____
_____
_____
_____

Goals Checklist

Don't feel like you need to check all these boxes every week. Start with a goal of perhaps 2 or 3 and build from there.

- [ ] Daily Mass
- [ ] Confession
- [ ] Daily Rosary
- [ ] Daily Readings
- [ ] Divine Mercy Chaplet
- [ ] Novena
- [ ] Volunteer at Homeless Shelter or Food Bank
  (or other Corporal Work of Mercy)

- [ ] Morning Offering
- [ ] Evening Prayer or Liturgy of the Hours
- [ ] Fasting
- [ ] Read a Saint Biography
- [ ] Angelus
- [ ] Give alms or a donation

first, Breathe

Breathe in ...
7 seconds.
Hold your breath ...
7 seconds.
Breathe out ...
7 seconds.

Repeat.

As many times
as you like.

second, Become aware of God's Presence

third, Thanksgiving

Lord, I realize that all, even myself, is a gift from you. Today, for what things am I most grateful?

fourth, *Reflect*

"And why are you anxious about clothing? Consider the lilies of the field, how they grow; they neither toil nor spin; yet I tell you, even Solomon in all his glory was not arrayed like one of these. But if God so clothes the grass of the field, which today is alive and tomorrow is thrown into the oven, will he not much more clothe you, O men of little faith?"
Matthew 6:28-30

fifth, *Examination*

Lord, open my eyes and ears to be more honest with myself. Show me what has been happening to me and in me this day. Today, how have I experienced your love?

sixth *Contrition*

Today, what choices have been inadequate responses to your love?

seventh, *Hope*

Lord, let me look with longing toward the future. How will I let you lead me to a brighter tomorrow?

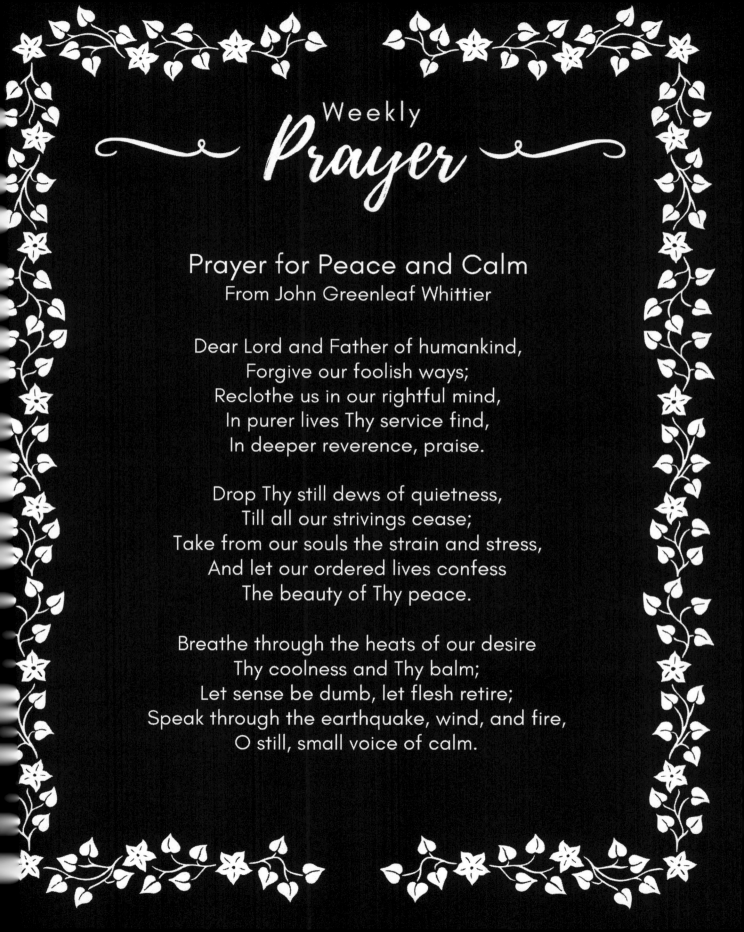

Weekly
Prayer

Prayer for Peace and Calm
From John Greenleaf Whittier

Dear Lord and Father of humankind,
Forgive our foolish ways;
Reclothe us in our rightful mind,
In purer lives Thy service find,
In deeper reverence, praise.

Drop Thy still dews of quietness,
Till all our strivings cease;
Take from our souls the strain and stress,
And let our ordered lives confess
The beauty of Thy peace.

Breathe through the heats of our desire
Thy coolness and Thy balm;
Let sense be dumb, let flesh retire;
Speak through the earthquake, wind, and fire,
O still, small voice of calm.

Prayer Goals

Prayer Intentions

For whom or what do you want to pray this week? In particular, consider praying for those who frustrate or anger you, maybe even those who have harmed you or your loved ones.

_____
_____
_____
_____
_____
_____
_____

As St. (Mother) Teresa said, "Not all of us can do great things. But we can do ... *small things with great love*"

List your "small things" below:

_____
_____
_____
_____
_____
_____
_____
_____
_____
_____
_____
_____

Goals Checklist

Don't feel like you need to check all these boxes every week. Start with a goal of perhaps 2 or 3 and build from there.

- [ ] Daily Mass
- [ ] Confession
- [ ] Daily Rosary
- [ ] Daily Readings
- [ ] Divine Mercy Chaplet
- [ ] Novena
- [ ] Volunteer at Homeless Shelter or Food Bank
  (or other Corporal Work of Mercy)

- [ ] Morning Offering
- [ ] Evening Prayer or Liturgy of the Hours
- [ ] Fasting
- [ ] Read a Saint Biography
- [ ] Angelus
- [ ] Give alms or a donation

first, Breathe

Breathe in ...
7 seconds.
Hold your breath ...
7 seconds.
Breathe out ...
7 seconds.

Repeat.

As many times
as you like.

second, Become aware of God's Presence

third, Thanksgiving

Lord, I realize that all, even myself, is a gift from you. Today, for what things am I most grateful?

"Though an army encamp against me, my heart does not fear;
Though war be waged against me, even then do I trust."
Psalm 27:3

fifth,
Examination

Lord, open my eyes and ears to be more honest with myself. Show me what has been happening to me and in me this day. Today, how have I experienced your love?

_____

_____

_____

_____

_____

_____

_____

sixth
Contrition

Today, what choices have been inadequate responses to your love?

_____

_____

_____

_____

_____

seventh,
Hope

Lord, let me look with longing toward the future. How will I let you lead me to a brighter tomorrow?

_____

_____

_____

_____

_____

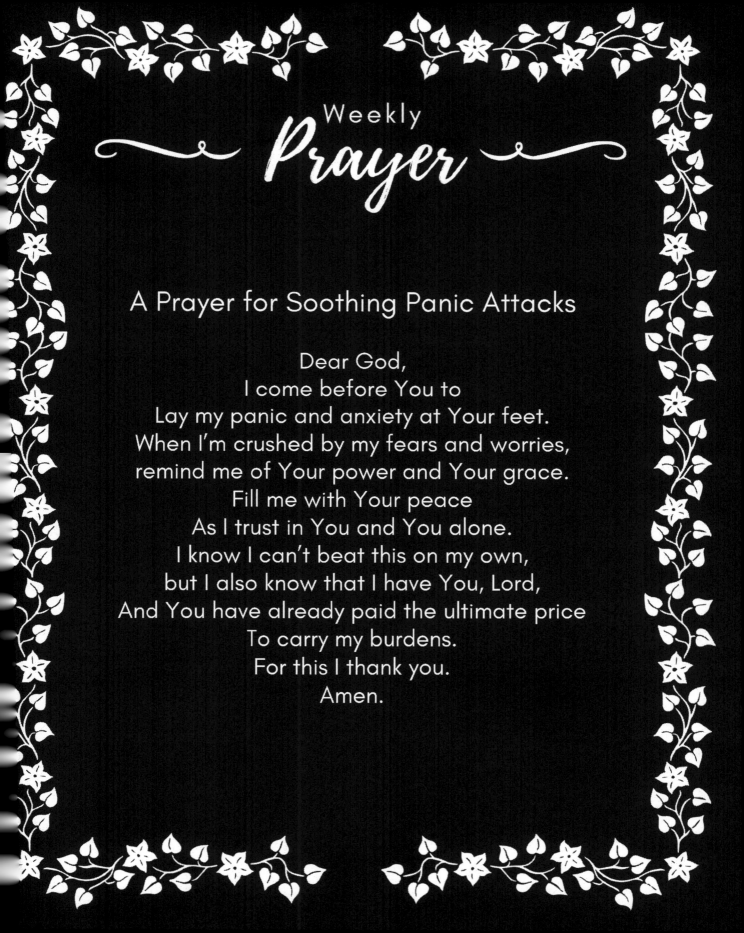

Weekly
Prayer

A Prayer for Soothing Panic Attacks

Dear God,
I come before You to
Lay my panic and anxiety at Your feet.
When I'm crushed by my fears and worries,
remind me of Your power and Your grace.
Fill me with Your peace
As I trust in You and You alone.
I know I can't beat this on my own,
but I also know that I have You, Lord,
And You have already paid the ultimate price
To carry my burdens.
For this I thank you.
Amen.

Prayer Goals

Prayer Intentions

For whom or what do you want to pray this week? In particular, consider praying for those who frustrate or anger you, maybe even those who have harmed you or your loved ones.

_____
_____
_____
_____
_____
_____
_____

> As St. (Mother) Teresa said, "Not all of us can do great things. But we can do ... *small things with great love*"

List your "small things" below:

_____
_____
_____
_____
_____
_____
_____
_____
_____

Goals Checklist

Don't feel like you need to check all these boxes every week. Start with a goal of perhaps 2 or 3 and build from there.

- ☐ Daily Mass
- ☐ Confession
- ☐ Daily Rosary
- ☐ Daily Readings
- ☐ Divine Mercy Chaplet
- ☐ Novena
- ☐ Volunteer at Homeless Shelter or Food Bank (or other Corporal Work of Mercy)
- ☐ Morning Offering
- ☐ Evening Prayer or Liturgy of the Hours
- ☐ Fasting
- ☐ Read a Saint Biography
- ☐ Angelus
- ☐ Give alms or a donation

first, Breathe

Breathe in ...
7 seconds.
Hold your breath ...
7 seconds.
Breathe out ...
7 seconds.

Repeat.

As many times as you like.

second, Become aware of God's Presence

third, Thanksgiving

Lord, I realize that all, even myself, is a gift from you. Today, for what things am I most grateful?

"Pain and suffering have come into your life,
but remember pain, sorrow, suffering are but the kiss of Jesus —
a sign that you have come so close to Him that He can kiss you."
- St. (Mother) Teresa of Calcutta

fifth,
Examination

Lord, open my eyes and ears to be more honest with myself. Show me what has been happening to me and in me this day. Today, how have I experienced your love?

_____
_____
_____
_____
_____
_____
_____
_____
_____
_____

sixth,
Contrition

Today, what choices have been inadequate responses to your love?

_____
_____
_____
_____
_____

seventh,
Hope

Lord, let me look with longing toward the future. How will I let you lead me to a brighter tomorrow?

_____
_____
_____
_____
_____

Weekly
Prayer

Your Peace

God,
Who is more than we can ever comprehend,
Help us to seek You,
And You alone.
Help us to stand before all that we could do
And seek what You would do,
And do that.
Lift from us our need
To achieve all that we can be
And instead,
Surrender to what You can be in us.
Give us ways to refrain from the busyness
That will put us on edge and off center,
Give us today Your peace.
Amen.

Prayer Goals

Prayer Intentions

For whom or what do you want to pray this week? In particular, consider praying for those who frustrate or anger you, maybe even those who have harmed you or your loved ones.

_____
_____
_____
_____
_____
_____
_____

As St. (Mother) Teresa said, "Not all of us can do great things. But we can do ... *small things with great love*"

List your "small things" below:

_____
_____
_____
_____
_____
_____
_____
_____

Goals Checklist

Don't feel like you need to check all these boxes every week. Start with a goal of perhaps 2 or 3 and build from there.

- [ ] Daily Mass
- [ ] Confession
- [ ] Daily Rosary
- [ ] Daily Readings
- [ ] Divine Mercy Chaplet
- [ ] Novena
- [ ] Volunteer at Homeless Shelter or Food Bank
  (or other Corporal Work of Mercy)

- [ ] Morning Offering
- [ ] Evening Prayer or Liturgy of the Hours
- [ ] Fasting
- [ ] Read a Saint Biography
- [ ] Angelus
- [ ] Give alms or a donation

first, Breathe

Breathe in …
7 seconds.
Hold your breath …
7 seconds.
Breathe out …
7 seconds.

Repeat.

As many times
as you like.

second, Become aware of God's Presence

third, Thanksgiving

Lord, I realize that all, even myself, is a gift from you. Today, for what things am I most grateful?

"If God sends you many sufferings it is a sign that He has great plans for you, and certainly wants to make you a saint."
– St. Ignatius of Loyola

fifth,
Examination

Lord, open my eyes and ears to be more honest with myself. Show me what has been happening to me and in me this day. Today, how have I experienced your love?

_____
_____
_____
_____
_____
_____
_____
_____
_____
_____
_____
_____

sixth,
Contrition

Today, what choices have been inadequate responses to your love?

_____
_____
_____
_____
_____
_____
_____

seventh,
Hope

Lord, let me look with longing toward the future. How will I let you lead me to a brighter tomorrow?

_____
_____
_____
_____
_____
_____
_____

Weekly *Prayer*

Prayer for Strength
From Psalm 27:1b

Dear Jesus,
You are the strength of my life;
You are my rock, my fortress and my protector;
Therefore, whom shall I be afraid?
You are my shield,
My strong-tower and my stronghold.
I will call to You because
You are worthy to be praised.
So, Father,
I thank you for being my strength
And My God in whom I trust.
Amen.

Prayer Goals

Prayer Intentions

For whom or what do you want to pray this week? In particular, consider praying for those who frustrate or anger you, maybe even those who have harmed you or your loved ones.

_____
_____
_____
_____
_____
_____
_____
_____
_____
_____

As St. (Mother) Teresa said, "Not all of us can do great things. But we can do ... *small things with great love*"

List your "small things" below:

_____
_____
_____
_____
_____
_____
_____
_____
_____
_____
_____

Goals Checklist

Don't feel like you need to check all these boxes every week. Start with a goal of perhaps 2 or 3 and build from there.

- [ ] Daily Mass
- [ ] Confession
- [ ] Daily Rosary
- [ ] Daily Readings
- [ ] Divine Mercy Chaplet
- [ ] Novena
- [ ] Volunteer at Homeless Shelter or Food Bank
  (or other Corporal Work of Mercy)
- [ ] Morning Offering
- [ ] Evening Prayer or Liturgy of the Hours
- [ ] Fasting
- [ ] Read a Saint Biography
- [ ] Angelus
- [ ] Give alms or a donation

first, Breathe

Breathe in ...
7 seconds.
Hold your breath ...
7 seconds.
Breathe out ...
7 seconds.

Repeat.

As many times
as you like.

second, Become aware of God's Presence

third, Thanksgiving

Lord, I realize that all, even myself, is a gift from you. Today, for what things am I most grateful?

fourth,
Reflect

"Never be in a hurry; do everything quietly and in a calm spirit. Do not lose your inner peace for anything whatsoever, even if your whole world seems upset."
– St. Francis de Sales

fifth, Examination

Lord, open my eyes and ears to be more honest with myself. Show me what has been happening to me and in me this day. Today, how have I experienced your love?

_____
_____
_____
_____
_____
_____
_____
_____
_____
_____
_____
_____

sixth, Contrition

Today, what choices have been inadequate responses to your love?

_____
_____
_____
_____
_____
_____
_____

seventh, Hope

Lord, let me look with longing toward the future. How will I let you lead me to a brighter tomorrow?

_____
_____
_____
_____
_____
_____
_____

Weekly *Prayer*

Prayer of St. Francis

Lord, make me an instrument of your peace:
where there is hatred, let me sow love;
where there is injury, pardon;
where there is doubt, faith;
where there is despair, hope;
where there is darkness, light;
where there is sadness, joy.

O divine Master, grant that I may not so much seek
to be consoled as to console,
to be understood as to understand,
to be loved as to love.
For it is in giving that we receive,
it is in pardoning that we are pardoned,
and it is in dying that we are born to eternal life.
Amen.

Prayer Goals

Prayer Intentions

For whom or what do you want to pray this week? In particular, consider praying for those who frustrate or anger you, maybe even those who have harmed you or your loved ones.

_____

_____

_____

_____

_____

_____

_____

> As St. (Mother) Teresa said, "Not all of us can do great things. But we can do ... *small things with great love*"

List your "small things" below:

_____

_____

_____

_____

_____

_____

_____

_____

_____

_____

_____

Goals Checklist

Don't feel like you need to check all these boxes every week. Start with a goal of perhaps 2 or 3 and build from there.

- [ ] Daily Mass
- [ ] Confession
- [ ] Daily Rosary
- [ ] Daily Readings
- [ ] Divine Mercy Chaplet
- [ ] Novena
- [ ] Volunteer at Homeless Shelter or Food Bank (or other Corporal Work of Mercy)
- [ ] Morning Offering
- [ ] Evening Prayer or Liturgy of the Hours
- [ ] Fasting
- [ ] Read a Saint Biography
- [ ] Angelus
- [ ] Give alms or a donation

first,
Breathe

Breathe in ...
7 seconds.
Hold your breath ...
7 seconds.
Breathe out ...
7 seconds.

Repeat.

As many times
as you like.

second,
Become aware of
God's Presence

third,
Thanksgiving

Lord, I realize that all, even myself, is a gift from you. Today, for what things am I most grateful?

"The secret to happiness is to live moment by moment and to thank God for what He is sending us every day in His goodness."
– St. Gianna Beretta Molla

fifth, Examination

Lord, open my eyes and ears to be more honest with myself. Show me what has been happening to me and in me this day. Today, how have I experienced your love?

_____
_____
_____
_____
_____
_____
_____
_____
_____

sixth, Contrition

Today, what choices have been inadequate responses to your love?

_____
_____
_____
_____
_____
_____

seventh, Hope

Lord, let me look with longing toward the future. How will I let you lead me to a brighter tomorrow?

_____
_____
_____
_____
_____
_____

Weekly
Prayer

I Want To Be Available

Holy and perfect God,
You know I want to be available.
Help that desire sink deeply enough
Into my being
For me to actually change
And to say "no" to a least one worthy,
But not urgent, task today.
Give me the ability to be open
To the life I am leading;
Not the one I am planning to lead.

Prayer Goals

Prayer Intentions

For whom or what do you want to pray this week? In particular, consider praying for those who frustrate or anger you, maybe even those who have harmed you or your loved ones.

As St. (Mother) Teresa said, "Not all of us can do great things. But we can do ... *small things with great love*"

List your "small things" below:

Goals Checklist

Don't feel like you need to check all these boxes every week. Start with a goal of perhaps 2 or 3 and build from there.

- [ ] Daily Mass
- [ ] Confession
- [ ] Daily Rosary
- [ ] Daily Readings
- [ ] Divine Mercy Chaplet
- [ ] Novena
- [ ] Volunteer at Homeless Shelter or Food Bank
  (or other Corporal Work of Mercy)
- [ ] Morning Offering
- [ ] Evening Prayer or Liturgy of the Hours
- [ ] Fasting
- [ ] Read a Saint Biography
- [ ] Angelus
- [ ] Give alms or a donation

first, Breathe

Breathe in ...
7 seconds.
Hold your breath ...
7 seconds.
Breathe out ...
7 seconds.

Repeat.

As many times
as you like.

second, Become aware of God's Presence

third, Thanksgiving

Lord, I realize that all, even myself, is a gift from you. Today, for what things am I most grateful?

fourth, Reflect

"You will never be happy if your happiness depends on getting solely what you want. Change the focus. Get a new center. Will what God wills, and your joy no man shall take from you."
– Venerable Fulton Sheen

fifth, Examination

Lord, open my eyes and ears to be more honest with myself. Show me what has been happening to me and in me this day. Today, how have I experienced your love?

_____
_____
_____
_____
_____
_____
_____
_____
_____
_____
_____
_____
_____

sixth, Contrition

Today, what choices have been inadequate responses to your love?

_____
_____
_____
_____
_____
_____
_____
_____

seventh, Hope

Lord, let me look with longing toward the future. How will I let you lead me to a brighter tomorrow?

_____
_____
_____
_____
_____
_____
_____
_____

Weekly
Prayer

A Prayer for Calming a Troubled Heart

Loving God,
Please grant me peace of mind
And calm my troubled heart.
My soul is like a turbulent sea.
I can't seem to find my balance,
So I stumble and worry constantly.

Give me the strength and clarity of mind
To find my purpose and walk the path
You've laid out for me.
I trust Your Love, God,
And know that You will heal this stress.
Just as the sun rises each day
Against the dark of night.
Please bring me clarity with the light of God.
In Your Name I pray.
Amen.

Prayer Goals

Prayer Intentions

For whom or what do you want to pray this week? In particular, consider praying for those who frustrate or anger you, maybe even those who have harmed you or your loved ones.

_____
_____
_____
_____
_____
_____
_____

As St. (Mother) Teresa said, "Not all of us can do great things. But we can do ... *small things with great love*"

List your "small things" below:

_____
_____
_____
_____
_____
_____
_____
_____
_____
_____
_____

Goals Checklist

Don't feel like you need to check all these boxes every week. Start with a goal of perhaps 2 or 3 and build from there.

- [ ] Daily Mass
- [ ] Confession
- [ ] Daily Rosary
- [ ] Daily Readings
- [ ] Divine Mercy Chaplet
- [ ] Novena
- [ ] Volunteer at Homeless Shelter or Food Bank
  (or other Corporal Work of Mercy)

- [ ] Morning Offering
- [ ] Evening Prayer or Liturgy of the Hours
- [ ] Fasting
- [ ] Read a Saint Biography
- [ ] Angelus
- [ ] Give alms or a donation

first, Breathe

Breathe in ...
7 seconds.
Hold your breath ...
7 seconds.
Breathe out ...
7 seconds.

Repeat.

As many times
as you like.

second, Become aware of God's Presence

third, Thanksgiving

Lord, I realize that all, even myself, is a gift from you. Today, for what things am I most grateful?

Peace I leave with you; my peace I give to you; not as the world gives do I give to you. Let not your hearts be troubled, neither let them be afraid.
John 14:27

fifth,
Examination

Lord, open my eyes and ears to be more honest with myself. Show me what has been happening to me and in me this day. Today, how have I experienced your love?

_____
_____
_____
_____
_____
_____
_____
_____
_____
_____
_____

sixth
Contrition

Today, what choices have been inadequate responses to your love?

seventh,
Hope

Lord, let me look with longing toward the future. How will I let you lead me to a brighter tomorrow?

_____
_____
_____
_____
_____
_____
_____

Weekly
Prayer

A Prayer for Christ's Peace

Lord, please put Your peace in my heart.
I'm worried and anxious.
My mind races and obsesses.
I can't help thinking about my problems.
And the more I think about them,
The more depressed I become.
I feel like I'm sinking down in quicksand
And can't get out.
Calm me, Lord.
Slow me down,
Put Your peace in my heart.

No matter what problem I have, Lord,
You are bigger,
You are more powerful than it is.
So I bring my problem to You.
I know what I want.
I know my will, but I do not know Yours.
I do not know how You will use this problem for my salvation.
I do not know what good You will work from this evil.
But I trust You.
I trust Your goodness and Your wisdom.
So I place myself in Your hands.
Please fill my heart with peace.
Amen.

Prayer Goals

Prayer Intentions

For whom or what do you want to pray this week? In particular, consider praying for those who frustrate or anger you, maybe even those who have harmed you or your loved ones.

_____
_____
_____
_____
_____
_____
_____

As St. (Mother) Teresa said, "Not all of us can do great things. But we can do ... *small things with great love*"

List your "small things" below:

_____
_____
_____
_____
_____
_____
_____
_____
_____
_____

Goals Checklist

Don't feel like you need to check all these boxes every week. Start with a goal of perhaps 2 or 3 and build from there.

- ☐ Daily Mass
- ☐ Confession
- ☐ Daily Rosary
- ☐ Daily Readings
- ☐ Divine Mercy Chaplet
- ☐ Novena
- ☐ Volunteer at Homeless Shelter or Food Bank
  (or other Corporal Work of Mercy)
- ☐ Morning Offering
- ☐ Evening Prayer or Liturgy of the Hours
- ☐ Fasting
- ☐ Read a Saint Biography
- ☐ Angelus
- ☐ Give alms or a donation

first, Breathe

Breathe in ...
7 seconds.
Hold your breath ...
7 seconds.
Breathe out ...
7 seconds.

Repeat.

As many times
as you like.

second, Become aware of God's Presence

third, Thanksgiving

Lord, I realize that all, even myself, is a gift from you. Today, for what things am I most grateful?

"In my deepest wound, I saw Your glory and it dazzled me."
– St. Augustine of Hippo

fifth,

Examination

Lord, open my eyes and ears to be more honest with myself. Show me what has been happening to me and in me this day. Today, how have I experienced your love?

sixth

Contrition

Today, what choices have been inadequate responses to your love?

seventh,

Hope

Lord, let me look with longing toward the future. How will I let you lead me to a brighter tomorrow?

Weekly
Prayer

Anima Christi

Soul of Christ, *sanctify me.*
Body of Christ, *save me.*
Blood of Christ, *inebriate me.*
Water from the side of Christ, *wash me.*
Passion of Christ, *strengthen me.*
O Good Jesus, *hear me.*
Within your wounds, *hide me.*
Permit me not to be separated from you.
From the wicked foe, *defend me.*
At the hour of my death, *call me*
And bid me come to you,
That with your saints I may praise you
Forever and ever.
Amen.

Prayer Goals

Prayer Intentions

For whom or what do you want to pray this week? In particular, consider praying for those who frustrate or anger you, maybe even those who have harmed you or your loved ones.

_____
_____
_____
_____
_____
_____
_____
_____
_____
_____

As St. (Mother) Teresa said, "Not all of us can do great things. But we can do ... *small things with great love*"

List your "small things" below:

_____
_____
_____
_____
_____
_____
_____
_____
_____
_____

Goals Checklist

Don't feel like you need to check all these boxes every week. Start with a goal of perhaps 2 or 3 and build from there.

- [ ] Daily Mass
- [ ] Confession
- [ ] Daily Rosary
- [ ] Daily Readings
- [ ] Divine Mercy Chaplet
- [ ] Novena
- [ ] Volunteer at Homeless Shelter or Food Bank
  (or other Corporal Work of Mercy)
- [ ] Morning Offering
- [ ] Evening Prayer or Liturgy of the Hours
- [ ] Fasting
- [ ] Read a Saint Biography
- [ ] Angelus
- [ ] Give alms or a donation

first, Breathe

Breathe in ...
7 seconds.
Hold your breath ...
7 seconds.
Breathe out ...
7 seconds.

Repeat.

As many times
as you like.

second, Become aware of God's Presence

third, Thanksgiving

Lord, I realize that all, even myself, is a gift from you. Today, for what things am I most grateful?

fourth, Reflect

For I know the plans I have for you, says the Lord, plans for welfare and not for evil, to give you a future and a hope.
Jeremiah 29:11

fifth, Examination

Lord, open my eyes and ears to be more honest with myself. Show me what has been happening to me and in me this day. Today, how have I experienced your love?

_____
_____
_____
_____
_____
_____
_____
_____
_____
_____

sixth, Contrition

Today, what choices have been inadequate responses to your love?

_____
_____
_____
_____
_____
_____

seventh, Hope

Lord, let me look with longing toward the future. How will I let you lead me to a brighter tomorrow?

_____
_____
_____
_____
_____
_____

Weekly
Prayer

A Prayer for Hope

Dear Lord,
I am your humble servant and
I kneel before You today,
Helpless and weak.
I need Your hope for love,
Kindness and for a better life, Lord.
I ask that You fill me from head to toe
With Your everlasting light.
Bathe me in Your glory, Lord,
And show me that everything is
According to Your plan.
Help me walk in Your glorious light and
Show me the path,
So that I may follow You in faith.
Amen.

Prayer Goals

Prayer Intentions

For whom or what do you want to pray this week? In particular, consider praying for those who frustrate or anger you, maybe even those who have harmed you or your loved ones.

_____
_____
_____
_____
_____
_____
_____
_____
_____

As St. (Mother) Teresa said, "Not all of us can do great things. But we can do ... *small things with great love*"

List your "small things" below:

_____
_____
_____
_____
_____
_____
_____
_____
_____
_____
_____
_____
_____

Goals Checklist

Don't feel like you need to check all these boxes every week. Start with a goal of perhaps 2 or 3 and build from there.

- [ ] Daily Mass
- [ ] Confession
- [ ] Daily Rosary
- [ ] Daily Readings
- [ ] Divine Mercy Chaplet
- [ ] Novena
- [ ] Volunteer at Homeless Shelter or Food Bank
  (or other Corporal Work of Mercy)

- [ ] Morning Offering
- [ ] Evening Prayer or Liturgy of the Hours
- [ ] Fasting
- [ ] Read a Saint Biography
- [ ] Angelus
- [ ] Give alms or a donation

first, Breathe

Breathe in ...
7 seconds.
Hold your breath ...
7 seconds.
Breathe out ...
7 seconds.

Repeat.

As many times
as you like.

second, Become aware of God's Presence

third, Thanksgiving

Lord, I realize that all, even myself, is a gift from you. Today, for what things am I most grateful?

"Hold your eyes on God and leave the doing to Him.
That is all the doing you have to worry about."
– St. Jane Frances de Chantal

fifth, Examination

Lord, open my eyes and ears to be more honest with myself. Show me what has been happening to me and in me this day. Today, how have I experienced your love?

_____
_____
_____
_____
_____
_____
_____
_____

sixth Contrition

Today, what choices have been inadequate responses to your love?

_____
_____
_____
_____
_____

seventh, Hope

Lord, let me look with longing toward the future. How will I let you lead me to a brighter tomorrow?

_____
_____
_____
_____
_____

Weekly
Prayer

A Prayer to Cast Out Fear

I know that worrying gets me nowhere.
Yet I still allow worry and anxiety to consume me.
In times such as these,
Lord Jesus,
I ask you to grant me
A great amount of strength, faith, and courage
To fight off the doubt and fear
Within my mind and heart.
Faith casts out fear
While fear casts out faith.

Prayer Goals

Prayer Intentions

For whom or what do you want to pray this week? In particular, consider praying for those who frustrate or anger you, maybe even those who have harmed you or your loved ones.

_____

_____

_____

_____

_____

_____

_____

As St. (Mother) Teresa said, "Not all of us can do great things. But we can do ... *small things with great love*"

List your "small things" below:

_____

_____

_____

_____

_____

_____

_____

_____

_____

_____

Goals Checklist

Don't feel like you need to check all these boxes every week. Start with a goal of perhaps 2 or 3 and build from there.

- ☐ Daily Mass
- ☐ Confession
- ☐ Daily Rosary
- ☐ Daily Readings
- ☐ Divine Mercy Chaplet
- ☐ Novena
- ☐ Volunteer at Homeless Shelter or Food Bank (or other Corporal Work of Mercy)
- ☐ Morning Offering
- ☐ Evening Prayer or Liturgy of the Hours
- ☐ Fasting
- ☐ Read a Saint Biography
- ☐ Angelus
- ☐ Give alms or a donation

first, Breathe

Breathe in ...
7 seconds.
Hold your breath ...
7 seconds.
Breathe out ...
7 seconds.

Repeat.

As many times
as you like.

second, Become aware of God's Presence

third, Thanksgiving

Lord, I realize that all, even myself, is a gift from you. Today, for what things am I most grateful?

fourth, Reflect

He will deliver my soul in safety from the battle that I wage,
for many are arrayed against me.
Psalm 55:18

fifth, Examination

Lord, open my eyes and ears to be more honest with myself. Show me what has been happening to me and in me this day. Today, how have I experienced your love?

_____
_____
_____
_____
_____
_____
_____
_____

_____
_____
_____
_____
_____
_____
_____
_____

sixth, Contrition

Today, what choices have been inadequate responses to your love?

_____
_____
_____
_____
_____
_____
_____

seventh, Hope

Lord, let me look with longing toward the future. How will I let you lead me to a brighter tomorrow?

_____
_____
_____
_____
_____
_____
_____

Weekly
Prayer

Memorare

Remember,
Most loving Virgin Mary,
Never was it heard that
Anyone who turned to you for help
Was left unaided.

Inspired by this confidence,
Though burdened by my sins,
I run to your protection
For you are my mother.

Mother of the Word of God,
Do not despise my words of pleading
But be merciful and hear my prayer.
Amen.

Prayer Goals

Prayer Intentions

For whom or what do you want to pray this week? In particular, consider praying for those who frustrate or anger you, maybe even those who have harmed you or your loved ones.

_____
_____
_____
_____
_____
_____

As St. (Mother) Teresa said, "Not all of us can do great things. But we can do ... *small things with great love*"

List your "small things" below:

_____
_____
_____
_____
_____
_____
_____
_____
_____
_____

Goals Checklist

Don't feel like you need to check all these boxes every week. Start with a goal of perhaps 2 or 3 and build from there.

- ☐ Daily Mass
- ☐ Confession
- ☐ Daily Rosary
- ☐ Daily Readings
- ☐ Divine Mercy Chaplet
- ☐ Novena
- ☐ Volunteer at Homeless Shelter or Food Bank (or other Corporal Work of Mercy)
- ☐ Morning Offering
- ☐ Evening Prayer or Liturgy of the Hours
- ☐ Fasting
- ☐ Read a Saint Biography
- ☐ Angelus
- ☐ Give alms or a donation

first, Breathe

Breathe in ...
7 seconds.
Hold your breath ...
7 seconds.
Breathe out ...
7 seconds.

Repeat.

As many times
as you like.

second, Become aware of God's Presence

third, Thanksgiving

Lord, I realize that all, even myself, is a gift from you. Today, for what things am I most grateful?

"Jesus, help me to simplify my life by learning what you want me to be and becoming that person."
– St. Thérèse of Lisieux

fifth,
Examination

Lord, open my eyes and ears to be more honest with myself. Show me what has been happening to me and in me this day. Today, how have I experienced your love?

_____
_____
_____
_____
_____
_____
_____
_____
_____
_____
_____

sixth
Contrition

Today, what choices have been inadequate responses to your love?

_____
_____
_____
_____
_____

seventh,
Hope

Lord, let me look with longing toward the future. How will I let you lead me to a brighter tomorrow?

_____
_____
_____
_____
_____

Weekly
Prayer

A Prayer for
Letting Go of Worries

Heavenly Father,
Lately I've been so worried about
Things that are out of my control.
Help me to trust that
You are working out
Every little detail of my life and
That I have nothing to fear
Or worry about.
In Jesus' name,
Amen.

Prayer Goals

Prayer Intentions

For whom or what do you want to pray this week? In particular, consider praying for those who frustrate or anger you, maybe even those who have harmed you or your loved ones.

_____
_____
_____
_____
_____
_____
_____

As St. (Mother) Teresa said, "Not all of us can do great things. But we can do ... *small things with great love*"

List your "small things" below:

_____
_____
_____
_____
_____
_____
_____
_____
_____

Goals Checklist

Don't feel like you need to check all these boxes every week. Start with a goal of perhaps 2 or 3 and build from there.

- [ ] Daily Mass
- [ ] Confession
- [ ] Daily Rosary
- [ ] Daily Readings
- [ ] Divine Mercy Chaplet
- [ ] Novena
- [ ] Volunteer at Homeless Shelter or Food Bank
  (or other Corporal Work of Mercy)
- [ ] Morning Offering
- [ ] Evening Prayer or Liturgy of the Hours
- [ ] Fasting
- [ ] Read a Saint Biography
- [ ] Angelus
- [ ] Give alms or a donation

first, Breathe

Breathe in ...
7 seconds.
Hold your breath ...
7 seconds.
Breathe out ...
7 seconds.

Repeat.

As many times
as you like.

second, Become aware of God's Presence

third, Thanksgiving

Lord, I realize that all, even myself, is a gift from you. Today, for what things am I most grateful?

fourth,
Reflect

"I have found the paradox, that if you love until it hurts,
there can be no more hurt, only more love."
– St. (Mother) Teresa of Calcutta

fifth,
Examination

Lord, open my eyes and ears to be more honest with myself. Show me what has been happening to me and in me this day. Today, how have I experienced your love?

_____
_____
_____
_____
_____
_____
_____
_____
_____
_____
_____
_____

sixth
Contrition

Today, what choices have been inadequate responses to your love?

_____
_____
_____
_____
_____
_____
_____
_____

seventh,
Hope

Lord, let me look with longing toward the future. How will I let you lead me to a brighter tomorrow?

_____
_____
_____
_____
_____
_____
_____
_____

Weekly
Prayer

Magnificat

My soul proclaims the greatness of the Lord,
My spirit rejoices in God my Savior;
For he has looked with favor on his lowly servant.
From this day all generations will call me blessed:
The Almighty has done great things for me,
And holy is his Name.
He has mercy on those who fear him
in every generation.
He has shown the strength of his arm,
He has scattered the proud in their conceit.
He has cast down the mighty from their thrones,
And has lifted up the lowly.
He has filled the hungry with good things,
And the rich he has sent away empty.
He has come to the help of his servant Israel
For he has remembered his promise of mercy,
The promise he made to our fathers,
To Abraham and his children forever.

Prayer Goals

Prayer Intentions

For whom or what do you want to pray this week? In particular, consider praying for those who frustrate or anger you, maybe even those who have harmed you or your loved ones.

_____
_____
_____
_____
_____
_____
_____
_____

As St. (Mother) Teresa said, "Not all of us can do great things. But we can do ... *small things with great love*"

List your "small things" below:

_____
_____
_____
_____
_____
_____
_____
_____
_____
_____
_____

Goals Checklist

Don't feel like you need to check all these boxes every week. Start with a goal of perhaps 2 or 3 and build from there.

- ☐ Daily Mass
- ☐ Confession
- ☐ Daily Rosary
- ☐ Daily Readings
- ☐ Divine Mercy Chaplet
- ☐ Novena
- ☐ Volunteer at Homeless Shelter or Food Bank (or other Corporal Work of Mercy)
- ☐ Morning Offering
- ☐ Evening Prayer or Liturgy of the Hours
- ☐ Fasting
- ☐ Read a Saint Biography
- ☐ Angelus
- ☐ Give alms or a donation

first, Breathe

Breathe in ...
7 seconds.
Hold your breath ...
7 seconds.
Breathe out ...
7 seconds.

Repeat.

As many times
as you like.

second, Become aware of God's Presence

third, Thanksgiving

Lord, I realize that all, even myself, is a gift from you. Today, for what things am I most grateful?

fourth, Reflect

"Come to me, all who labor and are heavy laden, and I will give you rest. Take my yoke upon you, and learn from me; for I am gentle and lowly in heart, and you will find rest for your souls. For my yoke is easy, and my burden is light."
Matthew 11:28-30

fifth, Examination

Lord, open my eyes and ears to be more honest with myself. Show me what has been happening to me and in me this day. Today, how have I experienced your love?

_____
_____
_____
_____
_____
_____
_____
_____
_____
_____

sixth, Contrition

Today, what choices have been inadequate responses to your love?

_____
_____
_____
_____
_____
_____
_____

seventh, Hope

Lord, let me look with longing toward the future. How will I let you lead me to a brighter tomorrow?

_____
_____
_____
_____
_____
_____
_____

Weekly
Prayer

A Prayer for Unburdening the Mind

Dear Loving Lord,
I am feeling stress, I am worried.
Too many things occupy my mind.
Won't you help me?
Show me, Lord,
Your order and Your plans are eternal.
Let me trust in Your Will alone.
Your Word tells me where there is love,
there is no fear.
Let me be filled with Your Love.
The perfect love
That tells me I am not condemned,
but I am saved.
I can do all things through You.
You strengthen me.
In Jesus name,
Amen.

Prayer Goals

Prayer Intentions

For whom or what do you want to pray this week? In particular, consider praying for those who frustrate or anger you, maybe even those who have harmed you or your loved ones.

As St. (Mother) Teresa said, "Not all of us can do great things. But we can do ...

small things with great love"

List your "small things" below:

Goals Checklist

Don't feel like you need to check all these boxes every week. Start with a goal of perhaps 2 or 3 and build from there.

- [ ] Daily Mass
- [ ] Confession
- [ ] Daily Rosary
- [ ] Daily Readings
- [ ] Divine Mercy Chaplet
- [ ] Novena
- [ ] Volunteer at Homeless Shelter or Food Bank
  (or other Corporal Work of Mercy)
- [ ] Morning Offering
- [ ] Evening Prayer or Liturgy of the Hours
- [ ] Fasting
- [ ] Read a Saint Biography
- [ ] Angelus
- [ ] Give alms or a donation

first, Breathe

Breathe in ...
7 seconds.
Hold your breath ...
7 seconds.
Breathe out ...
7 seconds.

Repeat.

As many times
as you like.

second,
Become aware of
God's Presence

third, Thanksgiving

Lord, I realize that all, even myself, is a gift from you. Today, for what things am I most grateful?

fourth, Reflect

"We should take as a maxim never to be surprised at current difficulties, no more than at a passing breeze, because with a little patience we shall see them disappear. Time changes everything."
— St. Vincent de Paul

fifth, Examination

Lord, open my eyes and ears to be more honest with myself. Show me what has been happening to me and in me this day. Today, how have I experienced your love?

_____

_____

_____

_____

_____

_____

_____

_____

_____

_____

_____

_____

_____

sixth Contrition

Today, what choices have been inadequate responses to your love?

_____

_____

_____

_____

_____

_____

_____

_____

seventh, Hope

Lord, let me look with longing toward the future. How will I let you lead me to a brighter tomorrow?

_____

_____

_____

_____

_____

_____

_____

_____

Weekly
Prayer

St. Francis' Canticle of the Sun

Be praised, my Lord,
For all your creatures,
And first for brother sun,
Who makes the day bright and luminous.
He is beautiful and radiant
With great splendor
He is the image of You,
Most high.
Be praised, my Lord,
For sister moon and the stars.
You placed them in the sky,
So bright and twinkling.

Prayer Goals

Prayer Intentions

For whom or what do you want to pray this week? In particular, consider praying for those who frustrate or anger you, maybe even those who have harmed you or your loved ones.

_____
_____
_____
_____
_____
_____
_____
_____

As St. (Mother) Teresa said, "Not all of us can do great things. But we can do ... *small things with great love*"

List your "small things" below:

_____
_____
_____
_____
_____
_____
_____
_____
_____

Goals Checklist

Don't feel like you need to check all these boxes every week. Start with a goal of perhaps 2 or 3 and build from there.

- [ ] Daily Mass
- [ ] Confession
- [ ] Daily Rosary
- [ ] Daily Readings
- [ ] Divine Mercy Chaplet
- [ ] Novena
- [ ] Volunteer at Homeless Shelter or Food Bank (or other Corporal Work of Mercy)
- [ ] Morning Offering
- [ ] Evening Prayer or Liturgy of the Hours
- [ ] Fasting
- [ ] Read a Saint Biography
- [ ] Angelus
- [ ] Give alms or a donation

first, Breathe

Breathe in ...
7 seconds.
Hold your breath ...
7 seconds.
Breathe out ...
7 seconds.

Repeat.

As many times
as you like.

second, Become aware of God's Presence

third, Thanksgiving

Lord, I realize that all, even myself, is a gift from you. Today, for what things am I most grateful?

"Let no one mourn that he has fallen again and again:
for forgiveness has risen from the grave!"
– St. John Chrysostom

fifth,
Examination

Lord, open my eyes and ears to be more honest with myself. Show me what has been happening to me and in me this day. Today, how have I experienced your love?

_____
_____
_____
_____
_____
_____
_____
_____
_____

sixth
Contrition

Today, what choices have been inadequate responses to your love?

_____
_____
_____
_____
_____
_____
_____

seventh,
Hope

Lord, let me look with longing toward the future. How will I let you lead me to a brighter tomorrow?

_____
_____
_____
_____
_____
_____
_____

Weekly
Prayer

A Celtic Prayer of Peace
David Adam

Calm me, Lord, as you calmed the storm;
Still me, Lord, keep me from harm.

Let all the tumult within me cease,
Enfold me, Lord, in your peace.

Calm me, Lord, as you calmed the storm;
Still me, Lord, keep me from harm.

Let all the tumult within me cease, Lord,
Enfold me in your peace.

Prayer Goals

Prayer Intentions

For whom or what do you want to pray this week? In particular, consider praying for those who frustrate or anger you, maybe even those who have harmed you or your loved ones.

_____
_____
_____
_____
_____
_____

As St. (Mother) Teresa said, "Not all of us can do great things. But we can do ... *small things with great love*"

List your "small things" below:

_____
_____
_____
_____
_____
_____
_____
_____

Goals Checklist

Don't feel like you need to check all these boxes every week. Start with a goal of perhaps 2 or 3 and build from there.

- ☐ Daily Mass
- ☐ Confession
- ☐ Daily Rosary
- ☐ Daily Readings
- ☐ Divine Mercy Chaplet
- ☐ Novena
- ☐ Volunteer at Homeless Shelter or Food Bank (or other Corporal Work of Mercy)

- ☐ Morning Offering
- ☐ Evening Prayer or Liturgy of the Hours
- ☐ Fasting
- ☐ Read a Saint Biography
- ☐ Angelus
- ☐ Give alms or a donation

first, Breathe

Breathe in ...
7 seconds.
Hold your breath ...
7 seconds.
Breathe out ...
7 seconds.

Repeat.

As many times
as you like.

second, Become aware of God's Presence

third, Thanksgiving

Lord, I realize that all, even myself, is a gift from you. Today, for what things am I most grateful?

"Without the burden of afflictions it is impossible to reach the height of grace. The gift of grace increases as the struggle increases."
– St. Rose of Lima

fifth,
Examination

Lord, open my eyes and ears to be more honest with myself. Show me what has been happening to me and in me this day. Today, how have I experienced your love?

_____
_____
_____
_____
_____
_____
_____
_____
_____

sixth
Contrition

Today, what choices have been inadequate responses to your love?

_____
_____
_____
_____
_____

seventh,
Hope

Lord, let me look with longing toward the future. How will I let you lead me to a brighter tomorrow?

_____
_____
_____
_____
_____

Weekly
Prayer

Prayer of Saint
Richard of Chichester

Thanks be to thee,
My Lord Jesus Christ,
For all the benefits Thou hast given me,
For all the pains and insults
Thou hast borne for me.
O most merciful redeemer,
Friend and Brother,
May I know Thee more clearly,
Love Thee more dearly, and
Follow Thee more nearly,
Day by day.
Amen.

Prayer Goals

Prayer Intentions

For whom or what do you want to pray this week? In particular, consider praying for those who frustrate or anger you, maybe even those who have harmed you or your loved ones.

_____
_____
_____
_____
_____
_____
_____
_____

As St. (Mother) Teresa said, "Not all of us can do great things. But we can do ... *small things with great love*"

List your "small things" below:

_____
_____
_____
_____
_____
_____
_____
_____
_____
_____
_____
_____

Goals Checklist

Don't feel like you need to check all these boxes every week. Start with a goal of perhaps 2 or 3 and build from there.

☐ Daily Mass

☐ Confession

☐ Daily Rosary

☐ Daily Readings

☐ Divine Mercy Chaplet

☐ Novena

☐ Volunteer at Homeless Shelter or Food Bank
(or other Corporal Work of Mercy)

☐ Morning Offering

☐ Evening Prayer or Liturgy of the Hours

☐ Fasting

☐ Read a Saint Biography

☐ Angelus

☐ Give alms or a donation

first, Breathe

Breathe in ...
7 seconds.
Hold your breath ...
7 seconds.
Breathe out ...
7 seconds.

Repeat.

As many times
as you like.

second, Become aware of God's Presence

third, Thanksgiving

Lord, I realize that all, even myself, is a gift from you. Today, for what things am I most grateful?

fourth, Reflect

Peace I leave with you; my peace I give to you; not as the world gives do I give to you. Let not your hearts be troubled, neither let them be afraid.
John 14:27

fifth, Examination

Lord, open my eyes and ears to be more honest with myself. Show me what has been happening to me and in me this day. Today, how have I experienced your love?

_____   _____
_____   _____
_____   _____
_____   _____
_____   _____
_____   _____
_____   _____
_____   _____

sixth Contrition

Today, what choices have been inadequate responses to your love?

seventh, Hope

Lord, let me look with longing toward the future. How will I let you lead me to a brighter tomorrow?

_____   _____
_____   _____
_____   _____
_____   _____
_____   _____
_____   _____
_____   _____

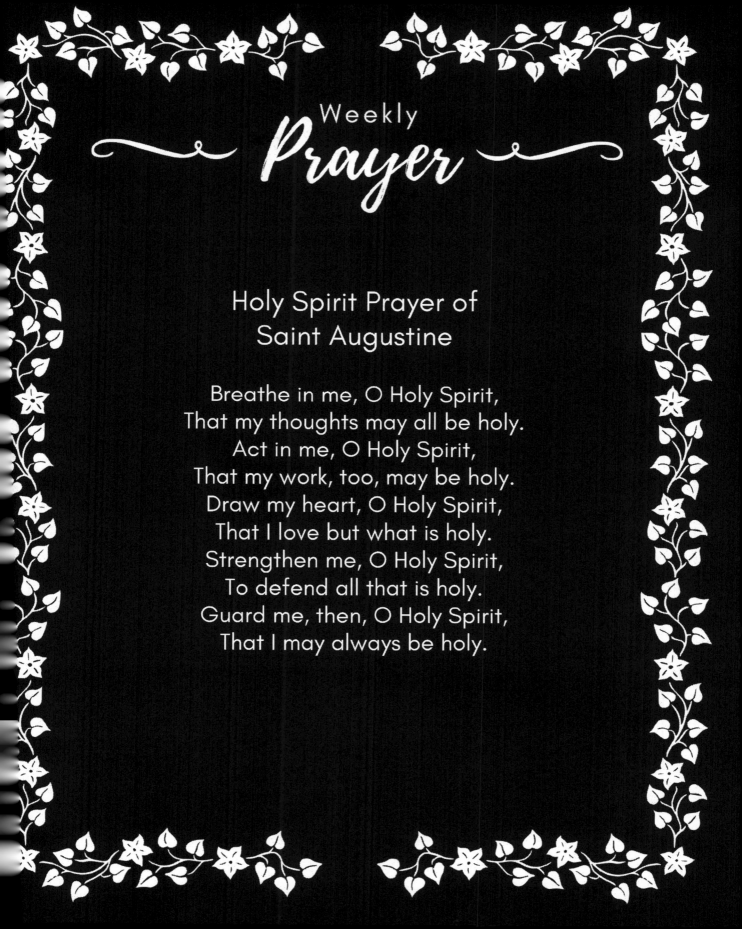

Weekly
Prayer

Holy Spirit Prayer of Saint Augustine

Breathe in me, O Holy Spirit,
That my thoughts may all be holy.
Act in me, O Holy Spirit,
That my work, too, may be holy.
Draw my heart, O Holy Spirit,
That I love but what is holy.
Strengthen me, O Holy Spirit,
To defend all that is holy.
Guard me, then, O Holy Spirit,
That I may always be holy.

Prayer Goals

Prayer Intentions

For whom or what do you want to pray this week? In particular, consider praying for those who frustrate or anger you, maybe even those who have harmed you or your loved ones.

_____
_____
_____
_____
_____
_____
_____
_____
_____
_____

> As St. (Mother) Teresa said, "Not all of us can do great things. But we can do ... *small things with great love*"

List your "small things" below:

_____
_____
_____
_____
_____
_____
_____
_____
_____
_____
_____
_____

Goals Checklist

Don't feel like you need to check all these boxes every week. Start with a goal of perhaps 2 or 3 and build from there.

- ☐ Daily Mass
- ☐ Confession
- ☐ Daily Rosary
- ☐ Daily Readings
- ☐ Divine Mercy Chaplet
- ☐ Novena
- ☐ Volunteer at Homeless Shelter or Food Bank
  (or other Corporal Work of Mercy)
- ☐ Morning Offering
- ☐ Evening Prayer or Liturgy of the Hours
- ☐ Fasting
- ☐ Read a Saint Biography
- ☐ Angelus
- ☐ Give alms or a donation

About the Authors

Sara A. and Scott L. Smith are currently in the 9th year of their honeymoon. *Pray, Hope, & Don't Worry* is the first published collaboration from husband and wife writing team of Smith & Smith, though they have already written many stories for their four young children. The Smith family currently resides in their shared hometown of New Roads, Louisiana.

Sara A. Smith (who goes by her middle name "Ashton") received her degree in Creative Writing from Louisiana State University. She has published multiple short works of fiction on Catholic themes.

Scott L. Smith is an author, attorney, and theologian. Scott is a lover of all things Catholic: the Eucharist, the Blessed Mother, and especially the King of Kings, Who is the hidden connection between all history, Scripture, culture, and theology.

Check out more of his writing and courses below ...

More from Scott Smith

Scott regularly contributes to his blog, The Scott Smith Blog, WINNER of the 2018-2019 Fisher's Net Award for Best Catholic Blog, found at www.thescottsmithblog.com:

Scott's other books can be found at his publisher's, Holy Water Books, website, holywaterbooks.com, as well as on Amazon.

His other books on theology and the Catholic faith include *Pray the Rosary with St. John Paul II*, *The Catholic ManBook*, *Everything You Need to Know About Mary But Were Never Taught*, and *Blessed is He Who ...* (Biographies of Blesseds). More on these below ...

His fiction includes *The Seventh Word*, a pro-life horror novel, and the *Cajun Zombie Chronicles*, the Catholic version of the zombie apocalypse.

Scott has also produced courses on the Blessed Mother and Scripture for All Saints University.

Learn about the Blessed Mary from anywhere and learn to defend your mother! It includes over six hours of video plus a free copy of the next book ... Enroll Now!

What You Need to Know About Mary But Were Never Taught

Give a robust defense of the Blessed Mother using Scripture. Now, more than ever, every Catholic needs to learn how to defend their mother, the Blessed Mother. Because now, more than ever, the family is under attack and needs its Mother.

Discover the love story, hidden within the whole of Scripture, of the Father for his daughter, the Holy Spirit for his spouse, and the Son for his MOTHER.

This collection of essays and the All Saints University course made to accompany it will demonstrate through Scripture how the Immaculate Conception of Mary was prophesied in Genesis.

It will also show how the Virgin Mary is the New Eve, the New Ark, and the New Queen of Israel.

Pray the Rosary with St. John Paul II

St. John Paul II said "the Rosary is my favorite prayer." So what could possibly make praying the Rosary even better? Praying the Rosary with St. John Paul II!

This book includes a reflection from John Paul II for every mystery of the Rosary. You will find John Paul II's biblical reflections on the twenty mysteries of the Rosary that provide practical insights to help you not only understand the twenty mysteries but also live them.

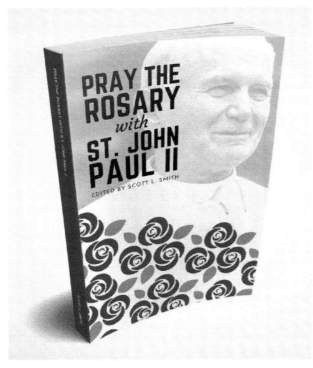

St. John Paul II said "The Rosary is my favorite prayer. Marvelous in its simplicity and its depth. In the prayer we repeat many times the words that the Virgin Mary heard from the Archangel, and from her kinswoman Elizabeth."

St. John Paul II said "the Rosary is the storehouse of countless blessings." In this new book, he will help you dig even deeper into the treasures contained within the Rosary.

You will also learn St. John Paul II's spirituality of the Rosary: "To pray the Rosary is to hand over our burdens to the merciful hearts of Christ and His mother."

"The Rosary, though clearly Marian in character, is at heart a Christ-centered prayer. It has all the depth of the gospel message in its entirety. It is an echo of the prayer of Mary, her perennial Magnificat for the work of the redemptive Incarnation which began in her virginal womb."

Take the Rosary to a whole new level with St. John Paul the Great! St. John Paul II, *pray for us*!

Catholic Nerds Podcast

As you might have noticed, Scott is obviously well-credentialed as a nerd. Check out Scott's podcast: the Catholic Nerds Podcast on iTunes, Podbean, Google Play, and wherever good podcasts are found!

The Catholic ManBook

Do you want to reach Catholic Man LEVEL: EXPERT? *The Catholic ManBook* is your handbook to achieving Sainthood, manly Sainthood. Find the following resources inside, plus many others:

- Top Catholic Apps, Websites, and Blogs
- Everything you need to pray the Rosary
- The Most Effective Daily Prayers & Novenas, including the Emergency Novena
- Going to Confession and Eucharistic Adoration like a boss!
- Mastering the Catholic Liturgical Calendar

The Catholic ManBook contains the collective wisdom of The Men of the Immaculata, of saints, priests and laymen, fathers and sons, single and married. Holiness is at your fingertips. Get your copy today.

NEW! This year's edition also includes a revised and updated St. Louis de Montfort Marian consecration. Follow the prayers in a day-by-day format.

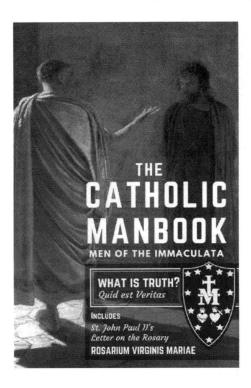
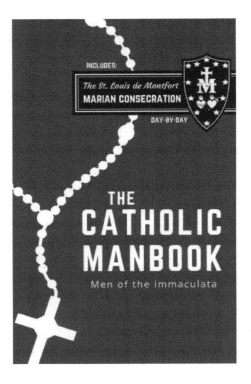

223

The Seventh Word

The FIRST Pro-Life Horror Novel!

Pro-Life hero, Abby Johnson, called it "legit scary ... I don't like reading this as night! ... It was good, it was so good ... it was terrifying, but good."

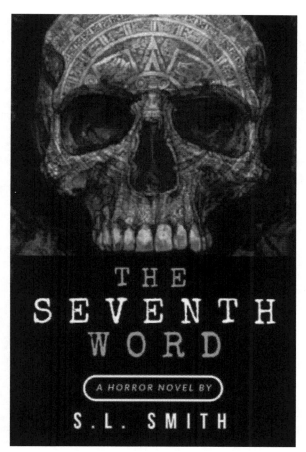

The First Word came with Cain, who killed the first child of man. The Third Word was Pharaoh's instruction to the midwives. The Fifth Word was carried from Herod to Bethlehem. One of the Lost Words dwelt among the Aztecs and hungered after their children.

Evil hides behind starched white masks. The ancient Aztec demon now conducts his affairs in the sterile environment of corporate medical facilities. An insatiable hunger draws the demon to a sleepy Louisiana hamlet. There, it contracts the services of a young attorney, Jim David, whose unborn child is the ultimate object of the demon's designs. Monsignor, a mysterious priest of unknown age and origin, labors unseen to save the soul of a small town hidden deep within Louisiana's plantation country, nearly forgotten in a bend of the Mississippi River.

You'll be gripped from start to heart-stopping finish in this page-turning thriller from new author S.L. Smith.

With roots in Bram Stoker's Dracula, this horror novel reads like Stephen King's classic stories of towns being slowly devoured by an unseen evil and the people who unite against it.

The book is set in southern Louisiana, an area the author brings to life with compelling detail based on his local knowledge.

Blessed is He Who ...
Models of Catholic Manhood

You are the average of the five people you spend the most time with, so spend more time with the Saints! Here are several men that you need to get to know whatever your age or station in life. These short biographies will give you an insight into how to live better, however you're living.

From Kings to computer nerds, old married couples to single teenagers, these men gave us extraordinary examples of holiness:

- Pier Giorgio Frassati & Carlo Acutis – Here are two ex-traordinary **young men**, an athlete and a computer nerd, living on either side of the 20th Century
- Two men of royal stock, Francesco II and Archduke Eu-gen, lived lives of holiness despite all the world conspir-ing against them.
- There's also the **simple husband and father**, Blessed Luigi. Though he wasn't a king, he can help all of us treat the women in our lives as queens.

Blessed Is He Who ... Models of Catholic Manhood explores the lives of six men who found their greatness in Christ and His Bride, the Church. In six succinct chapters, the authors, noted historian Brian J. Costello and theologian and attorney Scott L. Smith, share with you the uncommon lives of exceptional men who will one day be numbered among the Saints of Heaven, men who can bring all of us closer to sainthood.

THANKS FOR READING!

Totus Tuus

Made in the USA
Middletown, DE
10 August 2023